Elisa Segrave was b........................drid,
Berkshire and Sussex.........................and
Peru, and is the author of several unpublished ....ripts.
Between 1981 and 1990 she was married to the writer Andrew
Barrow. She has two children. Her articles and short stories
have appeared in the *Observer*, *Sunday Telegraph*, *Independent*,
Harpers and Queen, *London Review of Books* and in several
anthologies. Her first book, *The Diary of a Breast*, was
published by Faber in 1995.

by the same author

THE DIARY OF A BREAST

TEN MEN

ELISA SEGRAVE

faber and faber

To Duncan

First published in 1997
by Faber and Faber Limited
3 Queen Square London WC1N 3AU
This paperback edition first published in 1998

Typeset by Avon Dataset, Bidford-on-Avon, Warwickshire
Printed and bound in Great Britain by
Mackays of Chatham PLC, Chatham, Kent

Copyright © Elisa Segrave, 1997

Extract from *Lolita* by Vladimir Nabokov on p. 21 by kind permission of
Weidenfeld & Nicolson Ltd

Elisa Segrave is hereby identified as translator of this work in accordance with
Section 77 of the Copyright, Designs and Patents Act 1988

A CIP record for this book
is available from the British Library

ISBN   0–571–19223–8

2 4 6 8 10 9 7 5 3 1

My Father

When I was nine, my mother gave me a pamphlet about the facts of life, containing the phrase 'pass the seed'. It did not make much sense to me, so one day when I was alone at supper with my father I asked him to explain the sexual act to me. He did this without the least embarrassment. Our Catholic cook, Mrs Black (an alcoholic, it turned out), passed the food with a solemn face.

After this conversation I invented a term for the sexual act, 'doing spermia'. My father loved this phrase and immediately made up a song about a local woman, Hermia, whom he found attractive. He sang this song in the car as he drove along:

> I'm doing
> Spermia
> With Hermia.
> Spermia
> With Hermia's
> Great fun!

Until I was three, we lived in Madrid, where my father was naval attaché. He wore a white naval uniform. He held me up and I played with the medals on his jacket. My mother took me to see my father at work. His secretary called me Funny Face. I hated her. I hid my face in my mother's skirts.

At weekends my father pushed me up and down the Castellana – Madrid's main avenue – very fast in my pram. He called me Button-nose and was proud of me and my first sentence, 'Button-nose has buns for tea.'

One Sunday morning I was in my parents' bedroom.

'Go and ask Dad if he wants to go to the mountains today,' my mother said.

My father was sitting on the lavatory. 'Get out! Get out!' he shouted.

I ran back to my mother and put my head in her sheets.

My father loved singing. One of his favourites was this one:

> Hello! Hello! *Who's* your lady friend?
> *Who's* the little *Girlie* by your side?
> It wasn't the girl I saw you with at *Brighton*!
> I've seen *You*
> With a girl or two
> Oh oh *Oh*!
> I *am* surprised at *You*!
> Hello! Hello! Who's your lady friend?

My father had been sent to naval college aged twelve and had consequently been in the navy all his life. During the war he had commanded destroyers on the North Atlantic for four years and been decorated for bravery. He had been born in a caul – an extra membrane which surrounds some babies – and in the navy there was a superstition that if you were born in a caul you couldn't be drowned.

My father despised Scots, Americans, Peter Pan and Little Lord Fauntleroy. He thought all Scotsmen were pompous and he used to pronounce Robbie Burns as Rebbie Bairns, in an exaggeratedly mocking Scots accent.

Americans, my father had decided, were beyond the pale. They ate fried eggs on the same plate as jam and called the lavatory the john; even worse, according to my father, in America men sat beside each other on lavatories in open booths without doors.

Little Lord Fauntleroy was the popular children's book by Frances Hodgson Burnett. (My mother had had it as a child and passed it on to me.) Little Lord Fauntleroy, then Cedric Errol, was living modestly in an American town with his widowed mother. He was summoned to England by his paternal grandfather, an earl living in a stately home. My father found Cedric's sentimental name for his mother – 'Dearest' –

'absolutely nauseating', as he did the author's description of Little Lord Fauntleroy himself – 'golden lovelocks waving on his shoulders'. My father would repeat this phrase with a snort of derision.

As for Peter Pan, my favourite boy hero, the book about him was written by a Scot. It should not be taken seriously.

My father was capable of great acts of kindness, visiting people in hospital or lending them money. At the same time he made vicious remarks about those he considered ugly, hypo-critical or stupid. One woman, who attended the same Catholic church as we did, he nicknamed Evie the Bespectacled Cod. He disapproved of my mother's third cousin for attempting to hide her South American origins.

'Old Percy Farquhar said to me, "Pat's such a lovely English rose." I told him, "You bloody fool! She's half Peruvian!"'

Our local doctor, who had diagnosed a broken rib when my mother had pneumonia, was known as Half-wit. 'Half-wit always turns up before lunch, just in time for a drink,' my father guessed, probably correctly.

My grandmother's maid, Janet, also came under criticism for one idle remark: 'Old ladies don't eat much.' 'Your cousin Alice ate like a horse until she was a hundred!' my father insisted.

When I was three, my father left the navy and we returned to England, to live in a rented house on a common. I now had a brother, Jonathan, eighteen months younger than me, and a young nanny, Maureen. In our garden was a tiny shrubbery, full of yellow flowers. Here Jonathan and I used to play. There were wood pigeons cooing in the trees. On the lawn was a huge copper beech. Jonathan and I hid behind this tree and pulled each other's pants down. We were never caught.

In the evenings we danced to Scottish songs on an old-fashioned gramophone. My parents came and watched us. 'Over the Sea to Skye' and 'Bonny Dundee' were the favourites. On the gramophone lid was a picture of a dog, his head cocked, listening to His Master's Voice. This picture worried me. I thought the dog's master must have left him, and felt very sad.

3

I wanted my mother to pick me up, because of her soft skin. But she usually held Jonathan, because he was a boy. My father picked me up. One evening Maureen dressed us in each other's clothes, and at first my parents didn't notice. My mother picked *me* up, thinking I was Jonathan.

On special days we left the common and walked with my mother to an enormous lake. One summer the lake had dried up, and there was corn growing in it. My mother said proudly, 'Jonathan's hair's the same colour as the corn.'

I wished that I had blond hair like my brother. I pretended that my hair was gold, and that I was independent and courageous. The proof of my courage was my scarred knees.

We were on our way to the lake. My father came up behind us, with a strange woman.

'This is Sarah.'

I felt self-conscious.

'Sarah said you have very nice eyes,' my father told me that evening.

Why was it so important what Sarah thought? I could tell, however, that it mattered to my father.

My father appeared to like, or need, women, but he had a somewhat patronizing attitude towards them. He called those he was fond of Dear Little So-and-so. While in hospital having his appendix out, my father took a liking to a nurse whom he called Dear Little Jenny. My mother played along with it and she and my father went on referring to Dear Little Jenny for some time after my father had left the hospital.

By the time I was grown-up my father's first love, Sarah, whom he had met when he was a young sailor in Liverpool, had moved, with her third husband, to a village near my parents. She had been widowed during the war and, my father confessed, he had once 'done spermia' with her on a train. He had proposed to her, but she had refused him. He had then tried to prevent her from marrying her second husband, warning her, 'You won't get very far with him. He only fucks dukes' daughters!'

4

My father was mistaken. Sarah married the man in question and remained with him for several years.

In later life my father would often ring Sarah in the evenings and ask for help with the *Times* crossword. Once, after one of these long calls, her third husband, known as Lord Golf, because of all the time he spent on the golf course, telephoned my father back and yelled, 'Leave my wife alone!'

My father replied, 'Fuck off!'

Jonathan wasn't shy of people, but he was scared of other things. When we'd come back in the aeroplane from Spain, he'd been scared to sit in his seat. Maureen had put his toy tractor down first, to encourage him.

'There's his dear little tractor on the seat waiting for him!'

I despised Jonathan for being coddled. I was sure that women, including my mother, preferred him to me, just because he was a boy.

Once, when Maureen was mending Jonathan's pants, I asked why they had a hole.

'It's for his tail. You haven't got a tail.'

'You should have been the boy and Jonathan should have been the girl,' she added.

Jonathan was afraid of fireworks and he was afraid of the sea.

One afternoon my father drove me and Jonathan to a party. 'The party's in the barn,' an adult told us.

My father carried me across a farmyard in my white party dress. My brother followed. His buckled shoes got covered with mud. At the party we were separated. Jonathan didn't care, but I did. I sat close to Mary, who was at school with us. Usually I despised Mary. At her own birthday party she'd been allowed to stay in during musical bumps, because she'd cried. Jonathan and I used to invent imaginary tortures for her, such as cutting her in half or sticking a fork in her ear.

At teatime trestle tables were put side by side. There were oranges filled with ice-cream. I wanted to go to the lavatory,

5

but didn't dare ask an adult where it was. I saw Jonathan sitting several tables away. I knew he wouldn't mind asking, but I couldn't get to him.

We went to stay with my grandmother. I lay in a large bed, in a room with an orange carpet and peacocks on the curtains. I wet the bed every night.

Maureen scolded me, 'Jonathan only wets the bed once in a blue moon.'

I thought of a blue moon, a new moon, shaped like a thin crescent. What a funny thing to say!

When I was four, my brother Luke was born. We spent Christmas in London, as the new baby was born on 22 December. I was very excited. We went to the zoo, then we visited the baby and my mother in hospital. That evening, as I waited for the old-fashioned lift in the house where we were staying, I proudly recited his three names, 'Luke, John, Paul'.

Luke was mine from the start. I felt none of the jealousy I felt towards Jonathan, who, despite everything, was still my closest companion.

When I was six, my parents bought their own house, near my grandmother's in Kent. We were to stay with my grandmother for two weeks before moving in.

My mother was reading me a book at bedtime called *The Merry Meadow*, about a grasshopper, a rabbit and a harvest mouse who lived in a large meadow. The meadow was full of flowers and there was always sunshine.

'Will the new house have a Merry Meadow?' I asked my mother.

'Yes, the house does have a Merry Meadow,' my mother replied.

We did not realize we were in the Merry Meadow already, and would never find it again.

The day we left our rented house, where we'd been so happy for four years, was my seventh birthday. Maureen had left us, a few days before, because of a slipped disc, and we had an older temporary nanny, Nanny B.

Jonathan, Luke and I went with this new nanny to our

grandmother's, by car, sucking barley sugars. Our parents stayed behind in the rented house to pack up.

We arrived at my grandmother's around mid-day. She stood at the door to welcome us, with open arms. After lunch Jonathan and I went for a walk with her. Luke, now nearly three, stayed behind with the nanny. My grandmother explained that she had put wire round her big pond near the woods, to stop Luke falling in.

'I know Jonathan's already found a way round the wire,' she said to us. 'But you're both too big to fall into ponds.'

We went with my grandmother to see her pigs, then back across the big field to her house. It was November and the light was already fading. My grandmother stopped still every few minutes, to talk. She called it loitering.

'If you ever get lost in the woods, you can always find your way back by that big tree,' said my grandmother, pointing to the pine tree in her garden.

When she and I arrived back at the house, Jonathan wasn't with us. I went along to my mother's old schoolroom, to join Luke and the nanny.

Next door was the dining-room. It had brown panelled walls and portraits of relations with waxy yellow skins. My grandmother called them the Banana Faces. Her cook, Mrs Dashwood, had made a birthday cake for me, with white icing. There it was on the table, with seven pink candles and a sugar rose.

It was now completely dark and Jonathan still hadn't come back. All the adults had gone to look for him. I played a game with Luke, making him pretend to be a horse. We galloped up and down the corridor. In the corridor were two pictures, about a child being stolen by gypsies. In the first picture the gypsies, kneeling, with cruel eyes, surrounded the child in its white garments. In the second picture the child was shown back at home with its family, being kissed and washed and reclothed. I didn't believe the happy ending. For some reason, the first picture stuck in my mind.

Where was Jonathan? At last I decided to go and find out

what was happening. I sent Luke ahead of me along the corridor.
I heard someone say, 'Jonathan's in the water.'

I thought they meant the little fish-pond in the garden. An
adult sent us away. I took Luke with me back to the schoolroom.

Still no one came to see us. Again I opened the door into the
dining-room. My birthday tea was still laid out, and the cake
with candles, but there was no one to eat it. The yellow-faced
portraits stared down at me.

Much later my father came into the schoolroom and said,
'Jonathan's gone to heaven.'

'Oh,' I replied.

I tied Luke to the piano with a piece of string. He was my
companion from that day.

Hours later I opened my birthday presents. Someone had
given me a rubber, and put one in for Jonathan as well. Now it
was *my* rubber.

Beside the bed were pictures of wild boars. They looked very
cruel. My parents did not come to say good-night to me.

Our new house was much bigger than the old one. I sat outside
my mother's bedroom. I could hear her talking, to a woman
from the village, whose child had also died.

'Jonathan wasn't like the others,' said my mother.

I had always been jealous of Jonathan and now I hated him.
We would never be happy again.

My Catholic father arranged for me to have religious instruc-
tion once a week in a local convent. The nuns seemed scared,
running about like little mice. I was taught by Sister Camilla.
She led me past a picture of Jesus with his bleeding Sacred Heart,
into a sitting-room with ice-blue walls. The catechism book was
blue too. I had to learn the whole catechism by heart.

'Why did God make you?'

'God made me to know him, love him, serve him in this
world and be happy with him for ever in the next.'

I imagined God as a bald man sitting in the sky. I prayed on
my knees every night that I would enjoy my boarding school,

where I would go when I was eleven. Jesus, with his long hair and weak expression, did not appeal to me.

Every Sunday Luke and I went with my father to the Catholic Church next to the convent, to the ten o'clock Mass. It was a modern church, with a three-foot hand of God dangling over the altar. My father called it a ruddy great slab of meat.

He always marched to the front pew, which embarrassed us. Mass was bawled by Father O'Hara, who had a hoarse voice and a purple face. Although he often strode out with us before the end, my father was determined that we should follow the responses. At the consecration, when the host was held up, he would say to us loudly, 'Bow your heads, you little fools!' and at the 'Domine, non sum dignus', 'Strike your breasts, damn you!'

My father's mother, who had died when I was six, in a nursing home run by nuns, had, according to my father, been a strict Catholic and, even when he was a young midshipman, had sent him continual reminders of holidays of obligation. Another detail about his dead mother which seemed to preoccupy my father was that she had one sponge for her bottom and one for the rest of her body. Why did he find this so irritating and why did he mention it so often?

My father usually came down to breakfast in his dressing-gown and pyjamas. His pyjama cord was invariably undone and most mornings I saw his penis, surrounded by a mass of black hair, as he returned from helping himself to bacon and eggs.

At our new house my father was running a small farm, mainly beef cattle, with two men to help. Sometimes he went out and drove the tractor, but he also spent a great deal of time on the telephone, dealing with forms, bills, taxes and other administrative tasks.

In the house my father charged about like a caged animal. I do not remember ever seeing him relaxed. Even when making a simple telephone call, he would sit grasping the phone, rehearsing his words in a fierce undertone: 'Tell him to bloody well get the cows out of the field by the river. Tell him now!'

My father spent many afternoons in bed. There was a strong smell of feet in his room. My brother's nickname for my father was Big Buffalo.

In bed my father read, slept or did the *Times* crossword. He frequently did not emerge from his room till after tea. He then played his favourite records – *Gigi*, *My Fair Lady* and, in later years, *That Was the Week that Was*. He did not like the popular tune from *My Fair Lady*, 'I could have danced all night', but preferred the more robust 'I'm getting married in the morning', delivered by old man Doolittle. My father often sang this himself, with gusto. '"I could have danced all night",' he explained, 'is too sugary.'

After Jonathan was drowned I played with Luke all the time. We hid in the dark rhododendron bushes in our new garden. I pretended that he was an orphan and I was the only person in the world left to look after him. In a way this was true. My mother wasn't interested in him. The rhododendron bushes were our house.

We climbed on the hay bales up at the farm. I made my brother follow me over perilous heights and gave him points when he did as I said. I made him ride my pony. He hated riding because the pony often bucked and he fell off. I persuaded myself that he didn't mind. I wanted him to do everything I did.

I gave the orders. One of our games, called Cave, took place in low dark bushes near the disused tennis court. We were cave people, eating what we could find. Every so often I would yell, 'Dinosaur!' and we would both have to run like mad. If my little brother shouted, 'Dinosaur!' I would say firmly, 'Nonsense!' and refuse to move.

I arranged a code with my brother. If I said a secret word, he would have to leave whatever he was doing and come at once. I was always afraid that one day he would no longer follow me.

I had been to the dentist. One side of my mouth was numb. I bit and chewed it hard, so that it bled.

My mother was asleep on the sofa.

'My mouth's bleeding,' I told her.

'Of course the fish's mouth bleeds when the bait's in it,' my mother muttered.

She started moaning, 'I want Jonathan, I want my Jonathan.'

My new school was a few miles up the road. My father boasted to the head-mistress that I had read *Black Beauty* seven times when I was six. A horrible older girl came up to me at break. 'We all know what happened to your brother. The school was told before you arrived.' She had a narrow face, freckles, pale-blue eyes and a sly, mean expression. After she had said this, I loathed her.

Our English literature teacher, Miss O'Brien, was from Connemara. She taught us tragic poems, such as 'Lord Ullin's Daughter', about the chieftain's daughter who runs away with her lover in a storm. The girl's tyrannical father repents, too late.

> 'Come back! come back!' he cried in grief,
>   'Across this stormy water;
> And I'll forgive your Highland chief,
>   My daughter! Oh, my daughter!'

Miss O'Brien also made us learn other lugubrious poems, such as 'I Remember' and 'The Light of Other Days'.

> Oft, in the stilly night,
>   Ere slumber's chain has bound me,
> Fond Memory brings the light
>   Of other days around me:
>   ....
> I feel like one
>   Who treads alone
> Some banquet-hall deserted,
>   Whose lights are fled
> Whose garlands dead,
>   And all but he departed!

Who was this 'he' in the poem? Was it God, or an absent friend? I was afraid that I too would one day be completely alone. I imagined myself, a grown woman, wandering around Victoria Station, without any friends.

My father, like Miss O'Brien, and, indeed, myself, loved poetry and rhetoric. He had a brilliant memory for verse as well as some theatrical ability. (He boasted that as a young man he had made women in a pub cry by singing 'There'll be bluebirds over the white cliffs of Dover'.)

He taught us Alfred Noyes's poem 'The Highwayman', and he recited the counties of England, the southern ones to the rhythm of a horse trotting – 'Kent Sussex Hampshire Dorset Devon Cornwall' – and the northern counties to the rhythm of a horse cantering – 'Northumberland Durham and York, Lancashire Stafford North Wales'. He made us memorize the capitals of various countries as he drove us to school.

My father also enjoyed re-enacting scenes from his own life, often at the dining-room table. When he was in the navy in Australia, he and another young sailor had run over a dingo. My father had stopped the car and asked his companion to help him move the corpse on to the side of the road.

He had replied, 'Can't touch a dead dog, sir.'

My father was very scornful about this.

My father's own dog, Raven, was half black retriever and half Chesapeake Bay. His coat was curlier than an ordinary retriever's. Raven was extremely dignified, even as a young dog. He usually sat in the hall outside my father's study, paws crossed. His nose turned grey early on in life.

The only time Raven lost his dignity was when my father went shooting. The sight of the gun would make him delirious with excitement. He was not well trained and as soon as the gun went off, he would tear off to retrieve the bird, without waiting for a command.

My father, already notorious in the neighbourhood, was known as Bang Bang Bugger Man, because of his habit of missing pheasants and swearing. If one of us went with him, he would shout at us alternately, 'Come back, you bloody child! Come back, you bloody dog!'

Our Catholic cook, Mrs Black, seemed to have fallen in love with my father. One Good Friday she was drunk. The local Catholic church was packed and we couldn't all sit in the same row. During the Passion Mrs Black became sentimental. She kept leaning forward and tapping my father on the shoulder. My father didn't notice. When it was time for the congregation to file round the church to kiss the Cross, Mrs Black sprang up and started to follow him, saying loudly, 'Come on, we want something to eat.'

'No, no, men first,' I whispered, grasping her arm.

Mrs Black then sat down again, forgetting the Cross. My father made us all leave Mass early, as usual, but there were so many cars belonging to devout Catholics that he couldn't get out of the car park.

Mrs Black, who had insisted on sitting in front beside my father, nevertheless seemed very happy. 'Your daddy can get us out of anywhere!' she declared, as my father strode about the car park cursing.

After he finally drove off, she kept turning and smiling at him. She did it all the way home.

Soon after that Mrs Black had to leave because she was always drunk. Her son Tom, who was nineteen, was in a psychiatric home and used to come and visit her at weekends. After Mrs Black had left, my father received an odd letter, postmarked from the village where this home was. It said, 'Keep your right hand down, sir.'

The letter was signed Dora Black.

My father often told me, in a slightly mocking tone of voice, usually in front of her, how much he loved my mother. His nickname for her was Tubby Fatlump.

My mother had been what we children and my father called On Diet for as long as I could remember. Would my father have preferred her thinner? (He had said, on one occasion, to me, 'I

13

like big women, because you can get a good hold of them.')

He was always putting his arm round my mother and trying to kiss her, but my mother nearly always pushed him off. I quickly learned to do the same thing when my father tried to kiss me.

On their honeymoon my parents had gone to America, to meet my mother's aunt and cousins. Her American aunt had begged her to stay on in Florida while my father returned to his naval job in Plymouth.

'I told your great-aunt, "My wife is coming with me",' my father said. 'I wanted to go on doing spermia with your mother,' he explained to me.

My father took extreme attitudes towards my mother's American relations. When I was five, we had gone to visit them, in New York and Florida, sailing on the *Queen Mary*. Jonathan and I were photographed on deck arriving in New York harbour, wearing bonnets made of brown velvet. Luke had been a sturdy one-year-old, with blond curls and brown eyes. He had learned to walk on board ship, and the Americans called him Butch, because he was so strong and courageous.

My father already thought my mother's American aunt far too bossy, but the person he really couldn't bear was Clammy Sammy. (This was his nickname for the second husband of my grandmother's niece.) Clammy Sammy was a lugubrious handsome Pole with pale-blue eyes who said that during the war he had been in London working as a spy. My father said this was absolute nonsense.

My grandmother's nephew, whom my father called the Great Ape, raised cattle in Georgia. My father said that the Great Ape was 'practically certifiable', and, like most Americans, only cared about making money. According to my father, the Great Ape's first criteria for judging a fellow human being was to ask, 'Is he smart? Is he good at business?'

Presumably my father was not good at business, but had not tried to be. He had a small naval pension but, apart from this, the only money he attempted to earn now was through betting on horses. He placed his bets on the telephone with a bookie, first slamming the door so that my mother couldn't hear, then using his betting code-name, Ocean Bed. He usually lost.

Besides criticizing her relations, my father was also jealous of my mother's female friends.

One of these was Tatiana. She was Russian. She and her English husband, Johnny, had been great friends of my parents when they lived in Madrid. Johnny and my father still shared stupid jokes, even toys. On my father's desk when I was nine I found a yellow rubber Scotsman, four inches long, whose penis popped out from under his kilt when you squeezed him. Johnny had bought it in a joke shop. He had also sent my father a pen with a woman on it. Her clothes slowly rolled off her when you turned the pen upside down.

When I was thirteen, Tatiana went to hospital. She wrote a letter to my mother, telling her not to bring my father to see her as his voice was too loud.

My father, always conscientious about visiting sick people, was offended. Then when Tatiana subsequently came to stay, she complained about Raven, who used to growl softly while asleep. This irritated Tatiana.

'Tatiana kept telling me, "Stop him groaning!" so I told her to shut up,' said my father.

He still referred to this incident years later and never managed to forgive her.

'Tatiana used to look like a gazelle and now she looks like an old moose!'

My brother Luke, from being a bold chubby toddler with blond curls, had now changed into a slim nervous boy with olive skin, dark eyes and dark straight hair. He and I both had an identical birthmark, shaped like a small comma. Mine was on my right thigh, my brother's halfway down his right calf. These identical birthmarks made me feel even closer to him.

My brother was beautiful. Another of my mother's female friends, Maisie Prior, said he was like a Murillo painting. My father scoffed at this. He was jealous, both of my brother and of my mother's friendship with Maisie Prior. Why couldn't my mother take more notice of him?

He made up a song, to tease my mother, which he sang all over the house:

> Oh, I do love Maisie Prior!
> She never gets my ire!
> She is so calm,
> She's full of balm.
> Oh, good old Maisie Prior!

My father was worried that my brother showed no interest in cricket or any other sport. When his prep school said that my brother should be put in for a scholarship for Eton, my father, instead of being pleased, found it disconcerting.

'I hope he's not going to turn into a ruddy little intellectual!' he declared.

I too was often disappointed by my brother. I wanted him to be more courageous. While we were staying at my grandmother's for Christmas, he read all of M. R. James's ghost stories. In the story 'Oh, Whistle, and I'll Come to You, My Lad' the bedclothes rise up and take the shape of a person. My brother, alone in a two-bedded room, was petrified. He had to be moved to my mother's bedroom in the middle of the night.

I felt let down. Why couldn't he, a boy, be stronger? It made it worse that my mother seemed proud of his oversensitiveness.

Another time my brother was discovered cheating in Murder in the Dark. We all had to draw cards to decide who would be the murderer. Luke kept drawing the murderer card. Eventually we realized he was doing it on purpose. He had noticed that it was slightly bent in one corner. Did he choose the card because he was afraid of being murdered, or because being the murderer himself gave him a secret power?

His cheating ruined the game.

When I was eleven, I went as a boarder to the Convent of the Sacred Heart. Several of the girls in my dormitory didn't know the facts of life and I was able to get kudos by explaining to them about 'passing the seed'. The phrase became common currency in our class, where I also became popular for writing cheeky rhyming couplets about the nuns who taught us.

After three weeks my father wrote a letter to our head nun, Mother Monica: 'My daughter appears to be taking her religious duties in a very flippant manner and I am worried about it. On the other hand, the child is obviously happy and particularly enjoys the literature and French lessons.'

I had prayed on my own every night at home that I would like my boarding school and I did. But the public nature of school worship put me off religion. Before bedtime a Maltese nun came round the dormitories with a stoup containing a small sponge dipped in holy water. Sometimes, as she offered it to a girl in our dormitory, for her to make the sign of the cross, the nun would remark, 'Someone needs a footbath!'

This was not surprising as we were allowed to change our socks only twice a week. Our shirts, which we wore with a striped tie, were changed only once a week.

In the dormitory we were supposed to undress modestly, flapping underneath dressing-gowns. A horrible girl called Pam initiated 'stripping', where one girl would be primed to set on another girl unexpectedly and rip all her clothes off. Posy Harvill, who was in our dormitory, and rather disturbed – it was rumoured that she was adopted – used to lie on her bed with her nightdress up, opening and shutting her legs and making strange sucking sounds with her mouth. After a year she was expelled. No one was quite sure why. It was said that she had set off on her own one night looking for Teddy boys.

Teddy boys were supposed to be circling the school after dark and hiding in the woods. There was also a gardener's boy known as Baby Face, who was sighted every so often working in the vegetable garden. The only other male in the school, except for Father Hyatt, the priest, was red-faced Mr Eames, the singing-master, who commuted three times a week from London to teach us singing. His face purple with fury, Mr Eames would always contrive to lose his temper. He would point his conductor's stick at one of us, growling, 'Girl!' in a deliberately sadistic voice. He would then humiliate his chosen victim in front of the whole school. One girl, Lady Annabel Calvert, who already looked like a grown woman at fourteen, always stood her ground, refusing to be bullied by Mr Eames. It was thrilling for the rest of us to watch her defy him.

I didn't meet many males in the holidays either. One Christmas I went to a teenage party and danced all evening with a boy called Simon whom I had seen before at local parties and had always found intriguing. Simon usually stood apart, glowering, with a cap pulled down over his face. That night, however, he was friendly. After midnight he put his tongue down my throat several times and when two girls danced together beside us, to a Gerry and the Pacemakers record, Simon hissed, 'Lesbians!' I was devastated by his sophistication. I had only just learned the word myself, through stealing Simone de Beauvoir's book *The Second Sex* from my mother's bedroom drawer.

When I subsequently saw Simon at other teenage parties, he ignored me. He reverted to his former scowling routine, hanging about at the side of the room and never asking any of the girls to dance.

By now our whole neighbourhood seemed full of women that my father found attractive. There was Dear Little Jean over at Fairfield, Dear Little Hermia at Green Lane, Dear Little Ginny at Towick and Dear Little Moppie at Flimpton. My father was always reporting conversations he had had with Dear Little Moppie about her own daughters, who were slightly older than I was. One of them, a precocious girl who was considered very attractive and, indeed, thought herself so, was, according to her mother, nearly assaulted by a man in a first-class railway carriage.

'Dear Little Moppie told me that Camilla took off her high-heeled shoe and hit the man,' my father told us excitedly.

Normally at parties I was shy, but when Dear Little Moppie

gave a summer party for her daughters, I couldn't bear to be a wallflower.

Before I could get stuck into spending the evening alone, I overcame my shyness and boldly addressed a sandy-haired boy of my own age – fourteen – whom I liked the look of. He was even more timid than I was and seemed relieved to be approached. We danced together all evening. At midnight we were still going round and round the floor in the marquee, by now clutched together, his dry hot lips on my neck.

I'm sure Moppie, the hostess, didn't even notice her teenage guests; she was obsessed with her own two daughters' prowess. However, I felt that by dancing with this boy I had proved myself, not just in Moppie's eyes, but more importantly in my own, to be my father's daughter.

I was fined five pounds for climbing on the school roof. My father wrote another letter:

Dear Mother Monica

I am disturbed at my daughter's bad conduct. I have no doubt that you are justified in stopping her going out, but it does not seem to have much effect. You write that she is to be fined five pounds for climbing on a roof. I really don't see the point of this punishment; it means that I will have to pay, and in my view it is the responsibility of the school to devise a suitable punishment to deter the child from breaking the rules.

My wife is on a cruise in Cretan waters at the moment. She writes that she is much impressed with Rhodes and the old auberges of the knights of Malta.

After this letter I did not have to pay the fine. Nor did Hilary, my friend from Ireland, who had been on the roof with me.

Every evening at the convent we said prayers after supper, in the hall, in front of a hideous picture of Our Lady, known as Mater. (She was wearing red instead of the usual Our Lady's blue; her body was longer than her legs and she wore a crown of jewels. We were supposed to curtsy to Mater whenever we went past, even while carrying a pile of books. The more devout girls went into absurd contortions trying to do this.)

Occasionally after evening prayers a whole class was detained and there was an inquisition about a Terrible Incident. A girl in my class, who was top in sociology, had found her sociology exercise book torn up and stuffed down a lavatory. Our class was questioned for several minutes, but, although several girls blushed, probably out of nerves, no one confessed.

On Sunday evenings after supper we sang 'Salve, regina', in Latin. At the end we all sank in front of Mater in one dramatic curtsy. I liked the English translation of this prayer: 'To thee do we cry, poor banished children of Eve; to thee do we send up our sighs, mourning and weeping in this vale of tears.'

Was life on earth really so sad?

My father took an interest in my schoolfriends, and always told me which ones he liked. One weekend I took my friend Hilary home with me. My mother was on a trip abroad as usual and Juliet, a widowed friend of my mother, was staying, supposedly in order to help my father redecorate the dining-room.

My father seemed in rather a bad temper and left the table abruptly, before lunch was over, to go into his study.

'Shouldn't you have been making conversation with Juliet?' I asked my father that afternoon.

'What do you expect me to do, jump on her back and do spermia?' said my father rudely.

He became irritated with the redecoration plans and made the decisions in too much of a hurry, so that when I returned a couple of weekends later, the newly painted apricot walls clashed badly with our ice-blue chair-covers. Juliet, I gathered, had left before her week was up.

My mother was shy of talking about sex, but I had discovered that her bedside-table drawer was full of forbidden books – The Second Sex, The Perfumed Garden, the Kama Sutra, Fanny Hill, Lady Chatterley's Lover and The L-shaped Room. I borrowed these, usually for a night at a time, and returned them, without saying anything. (I took The L-shaped Room to school and passed it round our class, where several of us read it in turn, under the cover of *The Young Traveller in Belgium*.)

My father was far more open about his reading.

When I was thirteen, we went on holiday to Greece. My father was reading *Lolita*. He also had a paperback called *The Third Sex*, which he had bought at an Athens bookstall. I was intrigued. What on earth *was* the Third Sex? I tried to steal the book from my father, but eventually he became so annoyed that he threw it over the railings of the boat from Piraeus to Mykonos. He did lend me his copy of *Lolita*, however. It made a great impression on me, particularly the opening words: 'Lolita, light of my life, fire of my loins. My sin, my soul.' (I felt I knew all about forbidden love as I had a crush on Marina, a nonchalant and lazy Chilean girl in two classes above me at the convent. I wrote about our occasional encounters, in code, in a five-year diary my mother had given me for Christmas.)

On that Greek holiday my father, my brother and I returned home early, via Athens, leaving my mother on Mykonos with a woman friend.

My father's Greek friend, Stavros, was also in Athens, away from his wife, who lived in Paris. We all went to swim at a smart beach outside the capital, with a Swedish girl Stavros had picked up. My father told me on the way home that she had her period and that Stavros was irritated. She had accepted the beach invitation on false pretences.

That time in Athens I had a glimpse of my father's more sophisticated life. As a boy, he had loved being in France with his French cousins and later, as naval attaché, he had liked being in Madrid, where my parents had made many Spanish friends. When I see my father now, in photographs, thirty years later, he doesn't look English.

His mother was from a Jewish family, originally from Portugal, but my father and his sister claimed that she couldn't be Jewish, because by the time she was conceived her father had been too old to father a child. My father and his sister alleged that their mother was really the daughter of a dark-skinned English Catholic.

When I look back at my father, I wonder about his refusal to embrace his Jewish ancestry. Did he believe his mother was illegitimate? Perhaps she was.

My father was cultured, primitive, well read, musical, eccentric, generous, highly strung, instinctual and courageous. He had a strong sense of duty. Why was he so attached to the trappings of a conventional English upper-class life?

My Brother

My grandmother was worried that I didn't know any boys. I didn't like teenage dances any better than I had liked children's parties. We always did a Paul Jones, the girls and boys going round in opposite circles, hands joined. When the music stopped, you were supposed to dance with the boy opposite.

In the Paul Jones I often ended up facing Richard Booth-Browning. Richard wasn't all there, although he was usually very polite. He had big blue eyes with long black lashes, and pink cheeks. He seemed to like me better than the other girls and I hadn't the heart to be cruel to him. Also, he often made funny, off-beat remarks, such as 'No answer, the line's gone dead', when his hostess didn't reply to one of his questions.

My grandmother, who knew his grandparents, encouraged my association with him. When we met him at the local fête, she sent me off alone with him to the coconut shy, saying, 'Better a mad man than no man at all.'

My grandmother offered to throw a dance for me in her disused ballroom, where she usually let mice nest in the two old sofas. I wore a coral-coloured dress with white daisies sewn round the collar. My hair was done in an odd bouffant. I spent the evening smiling inanely.

My brother had said he wasn't coming, but at midnight he turned up in a taxi, in filthy corduroy trousers, with a mongrel puppy on a lead. He had just run away from school. I danced four times with Richard Booth-Browning.

At lunch the next day, after my brother had gone home with my parents, my grandmother said, 'I like everything to be normal. You do too, don't you?'

I replied, helping myself to raspberry pudding, 'Oh, Gran, I'm not sure.'

A few months after that my brother and I started taking drugs.

I dreamed I was in a runaway car. It was the time of the dance. I was driving my brother in my father's car and the brakes failed. We drove for a long time without brakes. We turned on to a long, empty, barren road where our mother stood with some guests who had been at the party. Suddenly I realized that we were coming to my grandmother's house. I drove in at the gates, relieved to be safe. I was afraid my grandmother would be angry.

My brother had not got a scholarship to Eton after all, but had gone there as an ordinary pupil. My mother, characteristically, had not gone with my brother on his first day at public school; she was on one of her trips to Russia. Her mother and my father had gone with Luke; my grandmother reported that he had been 'shaking like a leaf' as they approached the school.

My grandmother did not have the same feeling for my brother as she did for me; she said he was 'weak', adding, 'You can't do anything about that.' My father did not seem to know how to get on with his son.

At my brother's new boarding school, run by Catholic monks, he became friends with a group of intellectually precocious boys. The leader was Jerry, the son of an American scientist. Jerry, who was born with one leg shorter than the other, spent most holidays with his father and was *au fait* with the new hippie scene in America. Jerry brought marijuana back to school and he, my brother, my brother's friend William and two other boys smoked it regularly behind the bushes. After several months they were caught and expelled.

My brother had taken to marijuana immediately. Now he was keen to try different and more exciting drugs.

My friend Rose was attracted to my brother. My father, used to making comments on all my girlfriends, found Rose affected. 'She makes me feel quite sick!' he said unexpectedly.

At school Rose had not been popular with her peer group. She had been considered a slightly ridiculous figure, someone who paid far too much attention to her looks. She showed an early interest in boys and one autumn term she came back saying that she had engaged in 'heavy petting' that summer with a boy named Oliver, who had then abruptly gone into the priest-hood. She confessed all this to Mother Monica behind closed doors. The rest of us suspected that she did this not out of religious scruples but more out of a desire to make herself important.

Now, at seventeen, Rose and I were attending a tutorial college in London, to study for Oxford Entrance. My brother was at a progressive day school in Hampstead and we three met several times a week.

That summer Joseph, a much older man of thirty-two, had become Rose's first lover.

My brother and I were impressed by Joseph and what he stood for. He dealt drugs, mainly hash. He had dropped out of a successful career as a barrister and now lived in two rooms in a side street in Chelsea near Ossie Clark's shop Quorum. There was no bath; I found this bohemian rather than inconvenient.

Joseph was very thin and had a stringy yellow beard. Rose was striking, with her soft pale skin, jet-black hair and long flowing clothes. She did not favour the look favoured by my brother and me with our caftans, velvet trousers, Paisley shirts and rings from Afghanistan; she aspired rather to resemble a *Vogue* model. She got admiring glances in the street. I was terrified of getting admiring glances.

Joseph knew exciting men like Hoppy, who had started the *International Times*, London's first underground newspaper, and Steve Abrams, who had appeared on TV saying hash should be legalized.

When we went to see Joseph in the evenings, his front room was full of people in exotic velvet clothes, smoking. He called them 'heads' and had a revolving table built so that the joint could be passed more easily. One 'head', James, wrote single-line poems, like this one: 'He caught the frog that was in his throat.' James claimed to have reached a new level of spirituality, where words such as 'please' and 'thank you' were unimportant.

The 'heads' all wanted to destroy the System, and Joseph

said he did too. A year earlier he had owned an Alfa Romeo and a large flat in Belgravia with a studio and a black and white bathroom. Now he was rejecting this sterile life.

I was in awe of the 'heads', and embarrassed when Joseph introduced me as 'a schoolfriend of Rose'.

Every so often Rose encouraged me to get a boyfriend.

'Take a lover!' she would say grandly, as if this were the easiest thing in the world.

Rose, my brother and I arranged to go to Devon, by the sea, to the village where Luke and I had gone every year as children. Rose had been given some LSD by Joseph, and we planned to take it on the cliffs.

In the train Rose deliberately hitched up her skirt, so that my brother could see her knickers. I wished I hadn't introduced him to her. Her behaviour was vulgar and anyway she already had a lover – Joseph. What did she want with my brother?

Luke's character was noble compared with hers. He never made stupid jokes about sex like other boys of his age. Now, aged fourteen, I saw that he was beautiful. He was half boy and half man, still untouched. I felt guilty that he had met Rose through me. I was worried I might have sullied him.

Rose insisted that we take the LSD on the cliffs because she said it would be more beautiful up there. She was wearing a pale-mauve suit of flowing soft material which was more suitable for Ascot races. Luke and I wore almost identical Paisley shirts and jeans. Rose had had LSD once before. We never had.

On the cliffs there were dry pink flowers on the grass. A family of four were sitting on a bench, looking out to sea.

Behind me on the cliffs I thought I saw Rose's silhouette being dragged down the hill, every now and then tossing her head, flinging her long mauve scarf back. I was terrified. I imagined the family saying later, 'We've found a girl up here, obviously drugged.'

As I looked in the hot green swarming grass I saw that on nearly every pink flower was a caterpillar, a small furry yellow one with chocolate bars across his back.

I lay there staring out to sea, the lines on my hand burning red. Then a man with white hair came down the path, and I was afraid. I called to my brother to lead me back down the path, away from the cliffs, back to the village. Down by the sea-wall we had to pass two fishermen we had known as children. My brother stood, chewing grass. He was frightened. Neither of us dared speak to the fishermen. I felt now that there was a gulf between us and other people, because we had taken this drug. I didn't like it.

I went to bed in our room overlooking the sea. The sun was very bright. Rose came back, and played a record of Beethoven's Ninth Symphony very loudly. She told me and Luke to be quiet, as she liked listening to music when she was on a trip.

I thought how affected she was, and felt distant from her.

I had failed Oxford Entrance. Rose had passed, but I had only got on a waiting list. I went to hospital to have my tonsils out. It was terribly painful. My mother was on one of her trips abroad so my father came alone to visit me in Westminster Hospital. He stuck to a rule he had invented, of the visitor being allowed to eat the patient's fruit, and gobbled over half of a large bunch of black grapes. When I winced from spasms of pain, my father sat on my bed holding my hand very tightly, in silence. He was proud of this afterwards, and kept reminding me of it.

Before he left the hospital, my father told me, 'Your mother thinks she's going to be killed in an aeroplane crash.'

My mother turned up at my bedside two days later, holding a small bunch of violets.

Shortly after this I overheard a conversation my father was having in his study with one of his male friends. I heard my father saying that he thought that I was more attractive to older men. I was surprised. I wasn't particularly interested in older men, and the proprietorial way my father spoke of me, as though I were a cake in a cake-box waiting to be opened, made me feel uncomfortable.

Meanwhile, Rose kept nagging at me to 'take a lover'. She

suggested Gavin, a young naval cadet we had met at a party.

It was true that Gavin did seem keen on me. He was also very interested in my shoes, which he bent down to look at several times in the middle of the party.

I found Gavin rather old-fashioned. Certainly, he was far removed from the hippie circles my brother and I were interested in. He wore a suit and his own shoes were highly polished.

We went to a film together. He was nice-looking, with thick dark-blond hair, rich brown eyes and thickish, curling lips. After he had taken me out to supper one evening, I told him straight out that I wanted to lose my virginity and that he was the man I had chosen.

He was sharing a flat near Marble Arch. It was a hot July night. After returning from our meal, we both went upstairs to Gavin's attic room and took off our clothes. I noticed that his underpants were pale green. Or was this simply the colour they looked under the light of the street lamp? I couldn't be sure. Just before we went to bed, Gavin's flatmate, a young banker, returned. Gavin shouted downstairs to him, triumphantly. I realized that he wanted the other young man to know that he had a girl upstairs with him. This rather put me off.

I did not particularly enjoy the experience, nor did I dislike it. It was over rather quickly. Every so often, when I thought of Gavin in the next few months, I felt guilty that I had used him, and that he must have understood this. We did not go out together again. When I met him a year later, unexpectedly, at a respectable cocktail party, I felt embarrassed. He was still in the navy and was home for a few weeks on leave.

Three months later I found myself in digs on a main road in Gilmerton, a suburb of Edinburgh. It was my first term at the university. Heavy lorries went past the house at night. Inside, the walls were olive green. Mrs Browning, a sailor's wife, was very tidy. She wore soft twin-sets of angora wool in pastel colours and her blonde hair was immaculately wavy. She did not like me and Dorrie, the other student lodger, to have the electric fires on in our rooms and was careful to tell us to keep the lights off on the landing at all times. Her two boys boarded at the Edinburgh Academy and her husband was away at sea. She had a little daughter, Amy.

Dorrie came from Stirling and was studying German. She was the daughter of some friends of Mrs Browning, and was very respectable, like Mrs Browning herself, who seemed to lead a lonely life. Dorrie had spots and short black hair. She had never smoked dope and did not know anything about Bob Dylan or the Doors or the Incredible String Band.

Instead, I made friends with Chrissie, whom I had met at our freshers party. I had approached her because she was wearing a shirt of antique lace. I asked where she bought it, and she replied shyly, 'In a market in Scarborough.' Like me, Chrissie was studying English and, more importantly, she smoked dope. She came from Sheffield. Chrissie lent me the Bob Dylan records which I had left behind with my brother in London.

I played 'Just Like a Woman' on Mrs Browning's record player in her front parlour with its olive-green walls and dark-green sofas. Mrs Browning came in and told me to turn the music down.

In my bedroom I smoked some hash that Chrissie had given me, but I had to open the window to get rid of the smell and it was freezing.

In the bleak house in the late afternoons after my lectures Mrs Browning's little daughter, Amy, kept me company. She came into my bedroom and I brushed her hair and looked at her drawings. I was disappointed that she only wanted to play Mothers and Fathers. I was afraid that she would turn out like her mother.

About halfway through the term I began to get terrible pains in my stomach. They went on for several days. I was sent back to London to see the doctor, who prescribed Librium. Besides having stomach pains, my mouth was so full of ulcers I couldn't eat.

My brother and I went to our grandmother's. It was my nineteenth birthday. Her garden was full of brilliant autumn leaves, the creeper on her house a burning orange. Near the pond, where our brother Jonathan had drowned twelve years earlier, were two maple trees my grandmother had imported from America, their leaves scarlet.

My brother was wearing a purple velvet cloak which we had taken from our mother's cupboard; once again we joked and played the records we loved, 'Mr Tambourine Man', 'Queen Jane' and 'Sad-eyed Lady of the Lowlands'.

My grandmother sat calmly on the sofa, smoking Rothmans king size, occasionally dropping ash on to her bright-green cashmere cardigan.

I hadn't lost my brother after all.

I returned to Edinburgh and went to an appointment with the university doctor. My own doctor in London had arranged it. I managed to read some of his letter, which was lying upside down on the desk.

'These pains are psychosomatic. I think the girl misses her brother.'

David

After David had been sharing a flat for two weeks, I found myself wondering how to seduce him.

'Isn't he sweet?' I whispered to Chrissie, my friend from Sheffield.

It was my second term at Edinburgh and it was January. I had moved from my digs in Gilmerton and was renting a flat with two other students. David, six months younger than I, seemed very young indeed; his vulnerability and innocence were evident at once. He looked very English: fairish skin, pinkish cheeks, fairish hair, big innocent hazel eyes, beautiful bold bone structure, hair flopping over his forehead in a fringe. David, out of all the young men I had met, was the one who looked most like my grandfather, my mother's father, who had died in 1917, fighting in France, when my mother was three. David, like my grandfather, was, on his mother's side, from a military family. His mother had died when he was seven and he had been sent aged twelve to an army public school, where he had felt out of place.

He had Scottish grandparents and, before going to a Scottish university to study law in the autumn, was now up in the north for several months. At that moment he had a job as a hospital porter, in which he had to see dead bodies and dismembered limbs nearly every night.

In a way David's innocence was infuriating. I did not know the best way to go about seducing him, nor did I wholly know the reason why I wanted to, except that he was handsome and lived in the next room.

I was afraid that I had already appeared too independent.

I rehearsed in my mind what to say to him. Should I just say, in a sprightly way, 'Shall we go to bed?' or should I lie about late at night drinking Nescafé and looking seductive? The trouble was it would be difficult for me suddenly to change my manner.

I was shocked at the way I seemed, in my intention to seduce him, to have become ruthless.

I still missed my brother and I still hated Edinburgh, particularly now, this second term, in January, when it had got so cold and grey and sometimes snowed. When I was in the flat, I spent most of my time in bed.

David was always nice to me. In some perverse way I despised him for it. One evening he came and dropped festoons of food on to my bed – cheese and onion crisps, Swiss roll, Liquorice Allsorts. He told me that another boy we both knew had been to a party. I wished I had been there too.

A few days later – my parents had bought me a second-hand car – I drove with David towards the border, to Berwick. There were pine trees, red forests, the sky was boiling gold. For a moment we saw the sea – maned waves sprang at the sand. I remembered myself at other times. I told myself that eventually I would escape; I would not always be in Scotland.

That evening David came and sat on my bed and was very kind. We talked, but I felt it was like two waves hitting hopelessly against each other. When he went out of the room, a few seconds later I was worried to realize that I didn't remember what he looked like.

When I woke in the mornings, it was as though a great cliff were leaning over me; I tried to look round the darkness, but there was nothing. I thought that all I wanted was for someone to make love to me. Perhaps this would make me feel better.

From inside my shell I could hear myself speaking. I did not want to have to talk any more. I was tired of words. I wanted to be restored; I wanted my brother.

I did domestic chores with David. We went to get groceries in a fog. I drove the car through a pale-yellow light; almost without being aware of it, I felt subdued and peaceful in David's company. I was studying Wordsworth as part of my English literature syllabus. But I couldn't get involved. Instead, I remembered bits of *Paradise Lost*, Books 1 and 2, which had made a great impression on me aged fifteen at my convent:

> The mind is its own place, and in itself
> Can make a heaven of hell, a hell of heaven.

This was Belial, one of the fallen angels, arguing the case for not having a confrontation with God and fighting their way out of hell. But I was living in my mind already and it was hell most of the time.

Out of my own confusion I often felt aggressive towards David. I invented speeches with which to criticize him. I would say, 'I wish you wouldn't be so hearty. You never behave as though you know me. You have this absurd idea of separating the levels on which you talk to people. You think that people either have to have "polite conversation" or "deep talks". You think you are no good at the first and quite an expert on the second.'

Why did I have to be so mean? He was sweet and gentle.

We finally went to bed together. At first I thought it was the first act for a long time that had encouraged me and restored my self-respect. At the same time I was worried about my passivity in going to bed with David simply because we were sharing a flat. Also, he had only just left school. Inexperienced myself, I nevertheless saw myself as the older woman, teaching a beautiful young boy (David *was* beautiful) how to be a good lover.

David had a fine straight body; in bed his back had felt like silk. I liked touching him, but almost in a cold, appreciative way, like one would touch the man in Rodin's sculpture *The Kiss*.

At first I had clung to David; I thought he could be a wall. But then afterwards he spoke, looking exactly like a certain type of smooth man on cigarette advertisements, and this appalled me. I decided that in future I would not make my own body available for someone to practise on. I had thought earlier, when

33

I had planned to seduce him, that I could do it with detachment and still remain in control, but I couldn't.

To distance myself from David I now decided that I did not respect him in the least. Before we went to bed together, I had respected his innocence; he had seemed childlike, almost noble, but now he had resorted to the clichéd gestures of a man in an advertisement and this horrified me. I thought I had made someone cheap.

I persuaded myself that his innocence had not really been innocence, just transparent ground waiting to be trodden on.

The next day I decided not to go to bed with him again. I wrote cruelly in my diary: 'He is unsavable. I am never going to bed with young stupid people again. I shall not fall prey to the messy lips of boys.'

Nevertheless, our life in the flat went on. David did everything I wanted. He continued to bring me food in bed. He even helped me with my washing. If I wanted to go to bed with him – I changed my mind again about this – I just said, 'OK. Let's go to bed.' There wasn't anyone else in Edinburgh that I wanted to seduce, and he certainly was very beautiful.

In a way his obedience to me was gratifying. One night I shouted an order to him from my bed, to heat up a chicken pie. Did he *like* cooking for me? I wondered. Why did he do things for me? Perhaps he really did like other people telling him what to do.

I had talked a bit to David about my father and brother. He had been shocked when I told him about my father singing his song about doing 'spermia with Hermia' in the car, but I couldn't see why. This was what my father had always been like.

Another time I told David that I had occasionally wondered what it would be like to make love with my brother, although I knew I would never do it. He had seemed shocked by this as well, but later I thought – perhaps I imagined it – that he looked at me with a new respect.

Sometimes David told me stories of his own childhood. He had desperately wanted to please his father, an ex-fighter pilot.

But he was timid. He described one occasion, when he was four, when his father had wanted him to dive off a high diving-board – he had promised him an electric train – but he couldn't do it. He kept going to the edge of the board and looking over, but he still couldn't do it. He could only jump.

I was infuriated by his physical cowardice, but, in spite of myself, reluctantly pitying. Why did I not want to show any affection for David? For some reason I was afraid to let myself do so.

Towards the end of term another boy, Frank, arrived in Edinburgh. (I had met him while hitch-hiking with Chrissie.) Frank was different from David; he was extrovert, insouciant and cheerful. He had come to work for a term in a hostel for ex-prisoners, run by a Catholic priest whom he admired.

David became amazingly childish, I thought. He was jealous. He tried to pretend he didn't care that I liked Frank by whistling in a ghastly hearty way all over the flat. He calculatedly ignored me and tried to hurt me. 'Oh Lord, rid me of such pettiness!' I wrote in my diary.

I realized that I was very fond of him.

In March I got bronchitis for a long time and my parents came up to Edinburgh. As he had done before when I was ill, my father sat on my bed holding my hand in a firm grip, saying nothing. As before, he was very proud of this afterwards and kept mentioning it. My mother liked David, but my father seemed jealous. Once, when David was sitting in my bedroom while I was in my nightdress, my father burst in, looking furious, and David left the room. As for Frank, my father said he was 'so hideous he was only fit to be put in a circus'.

My father stayed on a few days longer in Edinburgh after my mother went south, as he wanted to visit an old girlfriend, Loveday, who was now married to a sheriff. One evening, while my father was out with Loveday, David and I went out. When we returned, my father was back already, asleep in the small spare room. He had defaced the note David had written to me earlier, calling me Sweetie-pie and suggesting we go out for black pudding and chips. My father had scribbled over David's writing in his own faint, forward-leaning, barely legible script: 'I have squitters and have gone to bed.'

Brother 2

In the summer term I left the university for a few days and went to Devon on my own, to the seaside village where we had taken LSD the summer before. I walked on the cliffs. The mist rose out of a chasm like a great white host, then it fell to pieces and drifted inland over the fields. A man I met up there said, 'It's rather beautiful, the mist coming up over the cliffs, isn't it, but very difficult for a fisherman trying to land.'

Later I went to sleep on the cliffs and dreamed of blackbirds that crawled like flies over a purple sky. I felt thirsty and imagined myself drinking out of a bottle of milk. It was nearly the summer holidays. My brother and I wanted to go to Glastonbury.

When I was back at Edinburgh, I dreamed that he and I did go there. It was on a golden hill, like a holy city. Later in the dream I watched an old-looking man, with long brown hair and a creased, wrinkled face, talking to someone I didn't know. I thought, what a weak-looking person!

Then I realized it was my brother.

David had gone south in the Easter holidays. His new job was as a kitchen porter in a hotel in Brighton. He did not return to Scotland for the summer term.

At the end of the summer I dropped out of the university. I had been there only one year.

My tutor, when I told him of my decision, said, 'I wish I was dropping out.' Nevertheless, he pointed out that if I regretted it, I could probably return at a future date and finish my degree.

Soon after, in July, my brother and I went down to Glastonbury in a van – six of us: me, Luke, his friend William, Jerry the American boy who was on crutches, Mandy (a girlfriend of William) and Vic, who illegally sold toys off a stall in Oxford Street. It was Vic's van.

We slept on the tor. In the morning there were long cushions of orange mist over the fields. The unfolding of the dawn.

Jerry's crutches looked luminous in the half dark.

William, who had taken a tab of LSD, said, 'There are corpses in front of us.'

'Nonsense', I said.

In the early morning a policeman came up the hill after us. (The night before Mandy had been causing a disturbance in the town by wildly running up and down the main street.) We watched the policeman, who must have been keeping an eye on us, toiling slowly over the wet green grass. William, from the top of the tor, pointed out Mandy, sleeping down by the gate. She looked like a bit of white sacking.

I walked down to her first. Her eyes, with small hard pupils, were pale blue ringed with black. She had long tangled russet hair. Everyone wanted to protect her, and she knew they did. She reminded me of the verse in Keats's poem 'La Belle Dame sans Merci':

> I met a lady in the meads,
> Full beautiful – a faery's child,
> Her hair was long, her foot was light,
> And her eyes were wild.

She knelt and stretched, her face corpse-white. She had great tufts of russet hair under her armpits, the colour of a fox. Her skin was rough, from not sleeping. She looked as if she wanted to be laid – ravished.

I told her that the policeman was coming down the hill to see her. The night before, when she ran up and down the main street, she had been wearing a long white nightdress trimmed with lace.

Now she took this garment off, and got another white dress out of a rucksack. She slid it over her head.

'He will not recognize me, yeah?'

The dress was exactly the same as the nightdress, except it was several inches shorter.

'My mother makes these dresses,' said Mandy. 'She's a good woman.'

Shortly after that I called on her in a Dorset village, where she was house-sitting. She was wearing a pale-blue sweater and a skirt. When I saw her in this different situation, I no longer saw her as an ethereal creature and I quickly lost the romantic feeling I had for her.

My brother and I were smoking hash through a Chinese water-pipe we had found at the house in Devon. Rose's boyfriend, Joseph, had sold us the hash earlier that day. Luke and I were wearing our almost identical Paisley shirts with flowing sleeves, and heavy carved metal rings that we had bought in Portobello Road. Mine had a green stone; his was coloured amber.

My brother said, 'You're a bully. You've always bullied me. You think you're so marvellous.'

'It's only people who allow themselves to be bullied that get bullied. You can't do anything on your own. You had to ring up Mum when you were hitch-hiking because you couldn't get back by yourself. You were hysterical.'

That night I dreamed my brother was chasing me on a motor-bike down a narrow lane. I kept losing him. Then I tried to ride the motorbike, but it was as though I were on the back of a tandem and couldn't get to the front. I kept falling off. I couldn't get the front straight.

How could I be with my brother all the time? How could I?

A few weeks later Luke and I went by train to see my grandmother. Although it was August, it was hailing when we arrived. My grandmother was wrapped in a mohair rug. She offered us drinks. My brother, now fifteen, asked for whisky, and Janet, my grandmother's maid, went reluctantly to get some out of a cupboard.

After lunch Luke and I went into the garden to smoke a joint. Flowers sprang out of the rain, mostly dahlias – bronze, gold and pink, with thin curved petals. On the lawn under the magnolia tree we met Janet returning from a walk with my grandmother's West Highland dog. They were both soaking wet. The dog rushed at us barking and I thought that Janet looked at us suspiciously from under her rain hat.

My brother and I walked for an hour through the ragged green woods in the rain. Down by the pond where Jonathan had drowned mammoth leaves flopped with water.

There was thunder that night. I dreamed there was an earthquake. The tree outside my window was down. The marble table in my bedroom had collapsed in a mess of rock.

In the morning we went to say goodbye to my grandmother before we took the train back to London. She was sitting up in bed having breakfast, wearing a pink bed-jacket, eating a croissant covered with bright-yellow butter. Her dog, lying on her bed, growled.

'What's important is to be good at Life, not to be clever,' said my grandmother, letting crumbs spill out of her mouth on to the eiderdown. 'I only want you both to be happy. Never mind about being geniuses.'

That night my brother, his friend William and I were standing in Portobello Road outside the Electric Cinema. We were about to see Buñuel's *Un chien andalou*. My brother loved anything surrealist. He loved the paintings of Magritte.

William told us, 'I've just read this: "The secret of human existence is to penetrate to the heart of human loneliness."'

'Yes, but what does it mean?' I asked.

William said, 'I don't know,' then added, 'Actually, I do know.'

I said I did too. But I didn't mind, because I had my brother with me.

I did not see William for some time after that. Then my brother told me that he had been put into Brixton Prison, for trying to kill his father with a knife.

It was the autumn of 1969. I was nearly twenty, my brother nearly sixteen. I was doing a typing course in Oxford Street and working in the mornings in the linen room of Westminster Hospital. I wanted to go to America. My brother was no longer living in Hampstead, but with me in our parents' London house, which my grandmother had bought for them. My parents were hardly ever there; they stayed mostly in the country. My mother sometimes came up for one night in the middle of the week. When my father came to London, he spent the day at his club.

My brother did not wash much and seldom wore underpants beneath his jeans. He had grown his hair very long. He enjoyed cooking more than I did and often made himself little dishes of pasta or shepherd's pie. He gave me domestic advice, such as telling me always to keep the handle of a saucepan on a cooker turned inwards so as to avoid getting scalded.

Often he prepared a ploughman's lunch for himself, using great chunks of white bread, Cheddar and Branston Pickle. He had begun to drink heavily, mainly cans of lager, but sometimes neat whisky.

One afternoon our mother arrived at the house unexpectedly and found some unwashed cups in the sink. My brother also used to make himself cups of tea, sometimes as many as ten a day. When our mother complained about the dirty cups, my brother was outraged.

'She's never even washed a plate for me in my whole life,' he said.

My mother was worried about my brother, although she admired him for demonstrating in Grosvenor Square against the Vietnam War. He was an idealist, she said.

In his bedroom in London she found a coloured photograph of an older man, in Holland Park, sitting with a group of long-haired people playing guitars. The man had hairy ears. My mother was sure he was a drug-dealer. She took the photograph to the local police station and asked if they knew him. But she did not get a satisfactory response.

A few days later my brother and I went for a walk on a stretch of wild country. It had once been a king's hunting forest. My brother insisted on swallowing some LSD which he had with him. He became distressed and began moaning fearfully. I helped him into the car and drove him to my parents' house, where he went to bed.

As my mother and I leaned anxiously over his bed, I did not dare tell her he had taken LSD.

Luke began to associate with a group of people I didn't know. He talked knowledgeably about different types of drugs and their effects, as if this inside knowledge gave him intellectual superiority.

I told him, 'It's not that clever to know those things. You might just as well learn all the different ways of cooking eggs.'

I was beginning to hate certain aspects of the drugs culture. I would never experiment to the extent that my brother, four years younger than me, had already done.

However, I thought he was more intellectual than I was and I respected this. He read high-powered books, often associated with drugs, such as *Opium and the Romantic Imagination*, William Burroughs's *Naked Lunch* and the stories of Borges, which he particularly admired. He smoked a great deal of hash, experimented with other drugs, drank whisky and beer, and now vodka as well. Was he already aware, at fifteen, of his self-destruction?

I knew that he felt a neglected child, an abandoned child, all his life.

The two of us often went to the Macrobiotic Restaurant off Westbourne Terrace. We sat on a floor in the dark basement eating brown rice and seaweed, both unusual in London then.

Other diners included American draft-dodgers wearing string vests and jeans. I got their addresses, hoping one day to go to America.

One evening we gave two of them a lift to Kilburn. My brother was by then taking drugs I didn't know about. When we stopped the car, for the couple to get out, Luke got out with them and was sick under a bridge.

As I watched him, I felt helpless. I was determined never to reach such degradation myself.

Two weeks later I had to go and bail Luke out from Chelsea Police Station in the middle of the night. He had been smoking dope in a flat in World's End with a group of people older than himself when the flat had been raided.

At his trial in Great Marlborough Street the magistrate gave him a smaller sentence than the two charged with him, saying, 'This boy comes from a good background and is younger than the others.'

His remark did not make sense. Surely, I thought, if my brother came from 'a good background', there was a case for saying that he should be more responsible?

Later that day my father telephoned me in London. 'Did you give him pot? Well, did you give him pot?'

He did not realize that my brother had been taking drugs for over two years. He seemed unable to cope with my brother and they did not appear to have much in common. After a few attempts to take him duck-shooting to an artificial pond by a river, my father didn't persevere. He had got the idea, like my grandmother, that Luke was weak and had given up on him.

My brother and I shared jokes about members of our family. He called my grandmother's white West Highland dog the Sugar Lump because of its white coat. He imitated my mother's voice, saying 'orf' instead of 'off' and spoke bitterly about what she referred to as 'my trips to Russia'.

Luke did not imitate our father, however, but talked admiringly of his eccentric behaviour, which had embarrassed us as younger children. He reminded me of the time we had both followed our father through Harrods, keeping some distance behind him because we were ashamed of his huge Russian fur hat with ear-flaps. He had bought it on a trip to Moscow with my mother.

Occasionally I used my brother as my protector, as I had that time when we had taken LSD together on the cliffs and I had been frightened to walk past the fishermen.

Now I was growing impatient about going to America, and didn't know how I would raise the money. One day while I was walking through Piccadilly I was approached by a short man with a square face who beckoned me and asked if I would like to be photographed for *Penthouse* magazine. I would be paid a hundred pounds.

'What if my father sees it?' I asked.

'We'll put a blonde wig on you and call you Susie.'

I said I would think about it. I arranged to meet him again in the same place at 7 p.m. This time I took Luke with me. The man seemed very nervous now as I told him I didn't want to be photographed after all. He didn't realize that my brother, who was well over six feet and had long wild dark hair, was a mild and gentle character.

One Sunday I went to visit my grandmother. My mother was there. I said, 'Luke's like he is because he feels incredibly guilty about Jonathan's being drowned.'

'But how can he think that? It was nothing to do with him.'

'I know. But he still feels responsible.'

'But I've always been very fond of Luke,' said my mother.

'Not when he was a little boy,' said my grandmother, in between sips of Old Fashioned.

In bed that night I couldn't sleep. I read some religious poems to soothe myself, but later in the night the faces in the macabre movie I had seen on television earlier – *What Ever Happened to Baby Jane?* – came back to me. I turned the light on. I heard someone on the stairs. I wanted to shout, 'Who is it?' but was too proud. It was Janet, the maid, letting out the dog.

The next day my mother telephoned and said my brother had got into trouble with drugs at day school and was coming home. The school had decided that my brother should take the rest of the term off as he was 'emotionally immature'.

He now had a girlfriend called Sheila. He had met her at a pop concert. She did not look at all like me, but had red bobbed hair, a turned-up nose and green eyes. Her mother was a masseuse in St John's Wood and her father had a private income. My brother moved into a flat with her, owned by her father. Her parents were divorced.

Sheila was an art student. While she went to art college on the tube, my brother stayed in her flat smoking hash, making tea in a Chinese tea-pot and reading more books – such as Sartre's *Nausea* and the stories of Edgar Allan Poe.

I felt a rivalry between Sheila and me. I had read a passionate letter, from her to Luke, that was lying around. It said: 'I long to kiss your beautiful nose.' I was shocked, and impressed, by her forwardness.

A few days after I read this letter I got out of our local underground station and saw Sheila, being kissed by a boy on the escalator. She was wearing a cloak the colour of oatmeal. She did not notice me and I did not say anything to my brother.

Shortly after that I received a telephone call in London from Sheila, saying my brother was in hospital.

'What's wrong with him?' I asked suspiciously.

'A drinking bout.'

When she added that she did not know which hospital he was in, I said, 'Surely you know.' I told her to telephone my mother.

My brother had once told me he was afraid of people. He had said pathetically, 'I want everyone to be nice to me.'

Two days later Luke arrived in London, looking like the Prodigal Son, his hair very long and wild. My mother arrived soon after. They went off to the country.

I dreamed I was with a strange man and my brother in a car. We came to a place where the path was crossed with branches; there was a hole. I knew the branches would break, but we tested them all the same. I was scared.

I couldn't decide whether to spend the night with my brother or with the man. I got lost. In my brother's bedroom was a dead body. I said, 'Don't look at it!' but he wasn't at all frightened. We uncovered it. It was a blonde girl, who slowly came alive. It was still horrible.

Then Rose came in, still in the dream. 'Someone's dead,' she said.

I took her arm sympathetically. 'Your brother?'

'Yes.'

I wanted desperately to go to America. I couldn't cope with Luke, though I felt guilty that I wasn't looking after him. My grandmother arranged with her American great-nephew that I would work as a very junior secretary in the company he ran in New York. My mother and I went to meet him for lunch at the Savoy Hotel, where he was on a flying visit. My father didn't come. He still despised Americans, saying that they were obsessed with making dollars.

The great-nephew, a man with a tanned face, huge blue eyes and untiring energy, gave me a short lecture, describing how he had worked his way up the company, starting as office boy.

'You'll have to learn to serve, my girl!'

Miss Sadler, his private secretary, with permed hair and an emerald suit, smiled benignly, and a bit warily, I thought.

A week later my grandmother's niece found me a room in the Barbizon Hotel for Women, on Lexington Avenue. I left for New York in November, just before my twentieth birthday.

I looked out of the aeroplane window at fields of snow and ice as we flew down the East Coast. The passenger beside me, a tiny lady with platinum-blonde hair, was reading *Valley of the Dolls* and eating peanuts.

I craned forward. Beyond the aeroplane's wing I could now see the skyscrapers of New York City, New York harbour and the Statue of Liberty, which I had first seen aged five, from the deck of the *Queen Mary*, with my two brothers.

Now I was supposed to be an adult, though I did not feel like one.

The aeroplane landed with a dreadful bump and the lady reading *Valley of the Dolls* screamed, spilling peanuts everywhere.

Martin

After I had travelled round America with Martin on Greyhound buses, my father wrote me a letter: 'If you marry this man, when the first flush of love is over, you will be left with a second-rate yobbo.'

Martin had a pink face and floppy brown hair, and was often out of breath. He wore glasses with thin rims and had small eyes. He was overweight and perspired.

I had met Martin twice in London, just before I went to America. I had been introduced to him by a friend of Rose, who worked for a publisher. Martin had spent the night in my parents' London house as he had nowhere else to stay. He had just finished a novel and Rose's friend was hoping his firm might publish it. It was written in the present continuous tense and, according to Martin, was highly influenced by a French writer, Michel Butor, whom Martin admired. (Butor, one of the practitioners of the *nouveau roman*, in France, had written a novel, also in the present continuous tense, called *Passing Time*. It was about a Frenchman who had spent a year in Manchester and hated it. Martin lent it to me. It reminded me of my life in Edinburgh and I only read a few pages before going into a terrible depression.)

By Christmas 1969 I had spent almost two months in New York as a junior secretary in my grandmother's great-nephew's office. In the early nineteenth century the company had been a romantic shipping line, with ships sailing between North and South America. Now it was a multinational making polymers and chemicals, sweets called Coffee Nips, synthetic fabrics, cereals, foil to wrap supermarket chickens, and many other products.

I was in public relations and communications, but I did not

relate or communicate. One of my tasks was to type captions for photographs, such as 'Technician stretches sperm over egg yolk', 'Proven bulls in barn', and so on. I secretly read Eldridge Cleaver's *Soul on Ice* under my desk. One morning I rang the office, pretending to have diarrhoea, and took the subway to Brooklyn Bridge to attend a rally to avenge Fred Hampton. (Fred Hampton, the former head of the Black Panther Party, had been shot in Chicago, allegedly murdered by US police.)

At the rally a black man with a punched-in nose sold me a copy of *Bulletin* magazine, which purported to advocate the overthrow of capitalism. I told him I was a secretary.

'Sick job. Soon there won't be no secretaries. You want to drop out, join the revolution,' he advised.

I did not know anyone in New York and the other young women at my hotel looked like models and secretaries or high-class call-girls posing as models and secretaries. On my first evening I had wandered into the library to be told by a glazed-looking librarian, 'No pant-suits in the library.'

'But this is a well-tailored pant-suit! It says in the hotel rules "Well-tailored pant-suits are acceptable",' I had argued, pointing to the chestnut-coloured matching top and trousers I'd bought in a Wallis shop before I left London. But she kept repeating, 'No pant-suits in the library', looking like a doll that should be on a shelf.

My only social life was the lunch-break in the office canteen where I made friends with two other young secretaries, American Fran, and Grace, who was Chinese. They, like Marine Harti, my boss in public relations and communications, had not had much contact with hippies and Fran especially disapproved of them.

Fran constantly warned me of the dangers of New York City, particularly of the subway, which, she said, was 'full of perverts'. As for Greenwich Village, one night a lorry driver there had shouted something out of his window at her and she had 'just stood in the street and screamed'.

Marine, my boss, when I told her that I frequently dropped

into Bookmaster's bookstore on 42nd Street after work, was also full of caution: '42nd Street is where the thieves and weirdos are!'

On my last day, after giving me my wages and some money that my grandmother had left in a bank in New York, Marine took me out to a restaurant in Chinatown, where we discussed Charles Manson. 'I think he's a pimp,' Marine said shrewdly. 'All those girls.'

She admitted that there were 'lots of good things about hippies', but her parting words, after handing me a box of Jardin du Bois soap which someone else had given her – 'If I use a different kind of soap, I break out,' she explained – were: 'I hear you're going to travel round America on a Greyhound bus. If you go on your own, wear a wedding ring and remember there are a lot of people in this country who are high on drugs.'

The next day I rang Martin in England, inviting him to come round America with me. I said I would meet him in Chicago, where I had decided to go in order to try to get into the Chicago trial. I had seen a girl at a pedestrian crossing on Lexington Avenue, wearing a yellow badge with the word 'Conspiracy' on it. I had chased her across the road to ask, 'What conspiracy?'

It referred to the Chicago trial, in which the US government accused Jerry Rubin and seven other 'revolutionaries' of 'conspiracy' to destroy the 1968 Democratic Convention in Chicago.

Martin accepted my invitation at once, rashly saying that he would pay for the trip with the two hundred pounds he had just been given by the publisher to rewrite his novel.

We agreed to meet five days later, in Chicago.

Next day I got out at Chicago's O'Hare Airport alone. I felt afraid, exposed and excited. The sky was blue, but there was a bitter wind. After collecting my suitcase, I went on the airport bus into town. On the bus I met a Spanish lady who took me with her to a hostel called Dearborn Residence for Girls. 'DO NOT GO OUTSIDE THE LOOP', said my guidebook; the hostel was well outside the Loop, I discovered that first night. During my three days there I made more friends than I had made in two months at the Barbizon Hotel for Women. My room-mate, Cathy, took me to visit her sister's farm in Indiana and Rosie-Anne, a young teacher from the Philippines, invited me to an all-day Filipino baptism.

I couldn't get into the Chicago trial. Despite the bitter weather, young people were sleeping outside the courthouse all night, desperate to be first in the queue. Instead, I took a bus to the University of Chicago, where I attended a meeting of the Students for a Democratic Society and sat in on one of Dr Bettelheim's lectures. (Bettelheim, a concentration camp survivor, was known particularly for his success with autistic children.) I hung about the university bookshop, where I found the following infuriating passage in *The Confessions of Alastair Crowley* (Crowley was one of the gurus of the hippie movement, and I had often heard various 'heads' quoting him admiringly): 'Morally and mentally women were for me beneath contempt. They had no true moral ideals. They were bound up with their necessary preoccupation, with the function of reproduction. Their apparent aspirations were camouflage. Intellectually, of course, they did not exist. Their attainments were those of the ape and the parrot.'

The morning after I read this I went to meet Martin at the airport.

Martin came out of customs wearing a grey overcoat. He told me it had belonged to his dead father and he was proud of it.

In the city we went and ate waffles and bacon in a downtown café. I still didn't know whether I thought Martin was attractive or not. Were we going to share a room? After reading my father's copy of *Lolita* at thirteen, on that holiday in Greece, I had nurtured the fantasy of travelling round American motels with a sugar-daddy. Martin did not fit into this category. Certainly he was nine years older than me, but, unlike Humbert Humbert in Nabokov's novel, he did not have any money. Also, he was overexcited and neurotic, and his brain worked very fast.

After breakfast he said we were going to find a hotel. There were four round the Greyhound Bus terminal. Martin chose one called the Atlanta. It had pale-green gargoyles over the door. I imagined they were the heads of famous mayors of Chicago.

The man behind the desk had a wart drooping over one eyelid. 'You're English, eh? How about Winston Churchill? Fine man, eh?'

He took us upstairs in a clanking lift.

'The lady sleeps here, you sleep here. Right, sir?' He opened two adjoining doors. 'Leave the keys back on the desk when you go out.'

Martin went into his room and shut the door. I did the same thing. I lay down on my bed. Out of the window was a fire escape. Down below some black porters in overalls were lugging boxes backwards and forwards into a lorry.

The door opened. It was Martin. 'Know how to look for bedbugs?' He lifted up the corners of the mattress with superior knowledge, making me feel young and ignorant. He sat down on the bed beside me and pulled out a list of underground newspapers. 'I said I'd collect these for a professor in England. He said he'd pay me. There should be one in every major US town . . . Right, we're going up Halsted Street now. Ready?'

I slung on my old brown car coat. Rose had given it to me. It had belonged to one of her aunts. The soft tattered fur round the neck, its shabbiness and the informality of its lack of buttons made me feel secure. The man behind the desk grinned at us as we left.

Martin swung left and we found ourselves on one of the bridges over the Chicago River. A man was standing there, his beard blowing into the wind. He looked like a symbol of freedom, but may just as easily have been in terrible despair. Martin was walking very fast and I had almost to run to keep up. I was borne along by his energy and by the dreadful wind at my back.

We had reached a wide street with tenement blocks scarred with broken windows. There were a few prams and washing-lines. We were the only white people around.

Martin looked anxious. 'Lucky you're wearing your trucking clothes,' he said, pointing to my bell-bottomed jeans. 'I'm going to get a taxi.'

We waited by a launderette under the grey sky. A yellow taxi drew up. The taxi driver thought Martin was a journalist.

'Why not get a job on the *Chicago Sun Times*, buddy?' the driver suggested helpfully. 'Just go into the offices. Why not? Give everything a try. There's money to be made in journalism.'

'Are you a Democrat or a Republican?' I asked.

'I'm a Republican, honey, and I dread the day when the Democrats take over this city. Now, here we are. Good luck, kids.'

'Oh, Christ. This doesn't look like a newspaper office,' said Martin. He banged on the door. A girl with chestnut hair in a Paisley dress opened it.

'Is this the *Seed* offices?' asked Martin.

She shook her head. Behind her, on a table, was a copy of *The Thoughts of Mao*.

'The offices used to be here. They moved out three months ago.'

An hour later we arrived at Chicago's main underground newspaper, the *Seed*.

The editor had a black beard. 'I've just been in jail for smoking marijuana.' He smiled cynically and somewhat proudly, I thought.

I sat down on a broken sofa. In front of me was a poster of a naked black man and two white girls, saying, 'Black is Beautiful'.

A smelly grey kitten climbed on to my lap. On the wall were cardboard pockets with different labels on them. One of them said, 'Manson'.

'May I look at this?'

'Sure.'

Inside was a photocopy of a letter:

Charles Manson 273803
Los Angeles Jail
An open letter to Evette J. Younger, District Attorney, Los
Angeles County
Dear Mr Younger
I am writing to you because I don't think I am getting a fair
trial. First of all I am an individual, one man, standing alone,
defending myself. You have hundreds of attorneys working for
you, hundreds of investigators working for you . . .

'Why do you have this?'

The bearded man looked up. 'We have to publish it. He's
not getting a fair trial. He's being exploited by the media. Jails
are terrible here. It's more like Turkey. People sit in jail for years
because they can't raise bail.'

Martin was in another part of the office leafing through back
copies of the *Seed*. I went and examined the noticeboard.
'SPEAK OUT ON ABORTION AND THE RIGHT TO CONTROL
OUR OWN BODIES IN THE MEDUSA TAVERN.' 'WANT TO JOIN A
COMMUNE? RING JOHN THE COMMUNE MAN.'

I turned to a boy with long, tangled hair. 'Are there lots of
communes here?'

He shook his head. 'They're mostly in California. Many of
them've degenerated. Like, they get money by panhandling and
stealing from supermarkets.'

We took a Greyhound bus next day, heading west across
America. In order to save money we slept several nights on the
bus, getting off at the terminals only to buy tuna fish sandwiches
and Coke out of the machines. At night Martin left me and
went to sleep in a seat on his own, his knees up and his head
hanging back into the passageway. I began to feel tender towards
him. He was unshaven and smelled of sweat, but I liked
having him near me. At the same time I resented my loss of
independence.

One evening the bus stopped for a few minutes in a small
town high up in the mountains. It was very quiet. The mountains

were huge and brown; halfway up, above the town, was a court-house with pure white columns, surrounded by cypress trees.

I got out and stood in the main street. Suddenly an awful loneliness possessed me. I was afraid I might cry. I started walking very quickly up the road.

'Where are you going?'

'To get some Kleenex.'

He came into the chemist after me. 'Hurry up, the bus is going . . . What's the matter?'

'Nothing.'

Back in the bus I sat forward, looking out of the window. All around were mountains and crushed rock, like a desert.

Martin put his arm round me. 'Look at this.'

'What is it?'

'It's this article about Sorel.'

'Who's he?' I forced myself to be interested.

'A French revolutionary who believed in violence.'

At dawn we got to Albuquerque. Square white houses on mud. We sat in the bus terminal waiting for the canteen to open. Opposite me were four little boys with dirty faces. Their mother looked harassed and had black patches under her eyes. One of the little boys kept wandering off and whining. She turned to a bigger one.

'All right, William, you'd better take him. I know he's just been.'

She grabbed another boy and wiped his nose. None of them was wearing any shoes.

The only hot food in the canteen was leathery scrambled eggs and hamburgers. The mother collected four mini packets of cereal and distributed them among the boys.

A woman in a printed dress went up to her. She was carrying a glass of milk.

'Here, have this. I don't need all of it.'

She then sat down opposite an oldish lady in a suit. 'Do you mind if I sit with you? I guess you're the only person that's human around here.'

Hours later we were in California. The houses had red flowers in their window boxes. The sky was red too as the bus swung into San Francisco.

'Is this the Golden Gate Bridge, do you suppose?'

Martin just grunted. We were among lines and lines of cars, the morning rush hour. My dress was wet with sweat – if I lifted up my arms I knew I would smell. We had not had a bath for days.

We found a hotel in Market Street with rooms for eight dollars a night – we were used to paying five – with a TV in each room. Market Street, we discovered, was the red-light district, or the tenderloin area, as it was called locally.

Martin lay on my bed thumbing through his list of underground newspapers.

'Right. We'll go to this bookshop, City Lights. They'll tell us where the newspaper offices are.'

We began our walk through the city. Hills and hills.

'It's more like a Turkish town,' said Martin. 'Look at the shutters on that office building. Look at the sun reflected on those shutters.'

A pale sunlight had begun to filter through the sky. It was a bit hotter than an ordinary English spring day.

That afternoon I walked alone through Chinatown. A boy with long hair handed me a piece of paper: 'WHAT IS CONSPICUOUS CONSUMPTION? IT IS THE PRACTICE OF CONSUMING THINGS TO IMPRESS OTHERS WITH YOUR WEALTH. ONE WEALTHY PERSON CONSUMES OVER 30,000 DOLLARS A MONTH WHILE CHILDREN STARVE IN CHINATOWN THREE BLOCKS AWAY. WHAT CAN YOU DO?

'IF YOU ARE POOR AND/OR ON WELFARE, JOIN WELFARE RIGHTS. IF NOT, AND YOU WANT TO LEARN AND/OR HELP, JOIN FRIEND OF WELFARE RIGHTS.'

Two men with malicious eyes were lounging against a wall.

'Give us a dime, sister,' said one.

Martin and I stood outside the offices of one of the town's main underground newspapers.

The door was opened by a man with hot red eyes and no shoes.

'Are any of the people here who run the *Good Times*?' Martin asked.

The man smiled half-wittedly and disappeared upstairs. His feet were the colour of a baboon's bottom.

We waited in a room with two old bicycles and the wax torso of a woman. Presently a girl in a sleeveless T-shirt came in. She had long wet hair under her arms.

'I was given this address by a man I met in a bookshop,' said Martin.

'Sure. Come into the kitchen.'

In the kitchen was a man with protuberant eyelids and hair like damp string. A girl in a Paisley dress was leaning over him, stroking him. The hairy girl joined her.

'The moon's in Scorpio. That's why you've got stomach ache. It's a bad day,' she told the man caressingly.

There were piles of coins on the kitchen table.

'That's what we made out of the last issue,' the hairy girl explained.

The girl in the Paisley dress went out of the back door into the garden.

'What's all this about the revolution?' Martin asked the man with protuberant eyelids.

'The revolution's already happened. These are "the good times",' he said in a tired sort of voice.

'See, Aquarius is a post-vidactic age following the age of Pisces, the age of Christ, where all unities merge,' said the girl with hairy armpits helpfully.

In the garden the other girl was staring absorbedly into a patch of earth. She spread her hands despairingly. 'No grass!' she shouted.

The hairy girl sighed. 'This is our third day without a smoke.'

A book of Saki's short stories was lying on a chair.

'Whose is this?' I asked.

'Someone must have left it here,' said the man. 'None of us

56

read books any more . . . except poetry, of course. Would you like to look at this? It's real acid poetry.'

I took the poetry book and opened it.

On screen I a burning red pin wheel distant amusement park.

'I think it's probably better if you read it on a trip,' I said.

He nodded with a melancholy expression. 'Who was that guy on the telephone?' he asked the hairy girl.

She pressed her lips to his head. 'He's just some wino I met. I said he could come in. Let's give him a try.'

The man sighed. 'I don't like him. He's on my mind.' He stared fixedly into space, then he turned to me. 'Would you like to see the rest of the house?'

The girl came with us. In the next room the man grabbed me and started chewing at my mouth. I thought it was rude to protest. The girl looked on in a good-humoured way.

Upstairs were two rooms, each with six mattresses on the floor.

'Do all those people live here?' I asked.

'Yes. You have to give up any idea of privacy.' The man grabbed me again and rubbed his hands up and down my back. I stood very stiff.

'Do you live off welfare?' I asked.

'Yes. We each get a hundred dollars a month.'

'Would you like some brown rice?' asked one of the girls in the kitchen. 'I'm just going to cook some.'

'No, we'd better go,' said Martin.

'Don't forget to go to Golden Gate Park tomorrow. Everyone goes there on Sunday to smoke grass on Hippie Hill.'

I was getting sick of Martin's intensity and the way he made me feel inferior. When we had had an ice-cream in an old-fashioned ice-cream parlour, he had made me feel he was only doing it to indulge me, that his mind was really on higher things. Why couldn't we do something frivolous for a change? I thought rebelliously. Martin's brain seemed to be speeding all the time, noticing things I would never notice, like the way the light fell on a certain building in Chinatown, or the shape of a bit of broken glass, but it was exhausting and I was beginning to feel that my perceptions were not my own.

I realized that by having asked Martin, a man I hardly knew who was nine years older than me, to come with me I had inadvertently put myself in a similar position to that of a young bride in an arranged marriage. I had thought it was liberated to telephone across the Atlantic and invite an unknown man to travel with me round a strange country. Now, I was trapped. Lolita at least had been travelling round motels with her lecherous stepfather against her will, and she had eventually run away. I had chosen to put myself in Lolita's position. I wasn't even having a romance, and I had ended up trapped anyway.

However, I had to admit that I had been in two minds about going the whole way across America on my own. I thought of something I had read in James Baldwin's novel *Giovanni's Room*, about a woman having to have a man.

'Don't you see, that's a sort of humiliating necessity?' said the character, whose name I didn't remember.

The next day Martin and I went to the terminal to catch the bus. I was in a bad temper.

'Look, don't forget to tell the driver you're going to break the journey and get off at Santa Barbara instead of going straight on to LA,' said Martin.

'I can't be bothered.'

'Don't be idiotic.'

Martin was reading a book on Shakespeare he had picked up in a secondhand bookstall.

'Shakespeare's a knockout,' he said. 'Listen to this . . . It's about two men who've renounced women in order to study . . . "The mind banquets while the body pines." Fantastic!'

What was I supposed to make of that? Had Martin renounced me already, in order to concentrate on his intellectual pursuits and his underground newspapers?

Out of the back of the bus I saw that the trees were light

green against a pink sky. The pink must be the result of dust or pollution, I decided.

Santa Barbara was in the mountains. We got there in the evening. Everything was in orange light.

'I'd like to stay here longer,' I said.

'That's what everyone says when they come. And a lot of them do stay.'

We went round looking for a hotel. Four of them refused us.

'There's something odd going on here,' said Martin paranoically. 'They can't all not have any rooms.'

'Perhaps they don't like the way I'm dressed,' I suggested. (I was wearing bell-bottomed jeans and a blue smock.)

Eventually we found a hotel, full of cockroaches. The first one we saw was on the front desk.

'What's that?' said Martin as it dashed under the register.

'Er, I guess it's a baby cockroach,' said the proprietor.

We went up in the elevator with a lady who muttered and churned spittle round and round in her mouth.

The next morning I walked on my own down the main street. I bought some liquorice chewing gum from a sweet shop.

'Well, the students really got down to it last night,' said the man behind the counter.

'What do you mean?'

'They burned down a bank here.'

'Was it in protest against the results of the Chicago trial?'

'I don't know what protest it was. I don't hold with violence. Now the hippies. They were all right. They weren't violent. But we're a peaceful town.'

I walked on, in the direction of the sea. I came to a vast white beach with palm trees. I lay on my back in the sand.

After a few minutes a man with short hair and a green shirt squatted down beside me. His eyes moved to and fro like a lizard's.

'You're English, huh? There are too many foreigners here. Soon as anyone wants some money in England they come over here, see Roosevelt, Eisenhower, Kennedy, have a dinner party

– go back with a million dollars. I reckon Ireland's a backward country and England's no different. Germany's the most progressive country nowadays.'

'What do you think of Reagan?'

'I reckon he's a movie star who shouldn't have become a politician. He's trying to do the right thing but the people won't go with him.' He pointed up the mountain to where there were several large houses. 'That's where Reagan should be. That's where all the movie stars live.'

'Do they have swimming pools?'

'Sure. They have swimming pools.'

'Do you think the police should have machine guns?'

'Sure. And use 'em whenever they have to . . . Should have used 'em last night on the students.'

'What do you mean?'

'Set of students burned down a bank here.'

'Oh! What do you think of the Vietnam War?'

'I reckon they should start from the south and go right through. If China gives any trouble, go through China, same with Russia. We could destroy 'em all. Destroy ourselves too . . . I see you don't agree with me.' He scooped up handfuls of sand and threw them down again.

'Well, don't you think there are too many rich people in this country?'

'I think everyone should be rich.' He moved closer. 'The hippies now, they're fools. They come down here and sleep on the beach. But there was a murder down here, the other night, so they've cleared off.'

'Who was murdered?'

'A hippie and his girl.'

He grinned unpleasantly. I sat there in silence.

He got up. 'Well, so long.'

I walked down the road. When I looked back, I saw him talking to a little boy building a sand castle.

'Jack Kerouac hitched down this coast,' I told Martin at the Santa Barbara bus terminal. 'By the way, someone told me that two hippies were murdered on the beach here the other night.'

'It wasn't hippies. It was a professor and his wife. I read it in the paper.'

It took four hours to get to LA. It was raining when we arrived. We went to a hotel opposite the bus terminal. As we were entering the elevator, a tall black man approached us.

'Want to score a lid?'

'I don't smoke while I'm in America,' said Martin pompously.

Two young men were waiting for the elevator on the third floor. As I stepped out, one of them slapped me on the behind. His companion looked at me apologetically.

'We're soldiers. We just got back from Vietnam. We haven't seen any proper women for months.'

My room was small and damp. There were drawings of crabs on the walls.

The next morning it was still raining. The street outside our hotel was full of bookstalls selling pornography. We took a bus to another part of town.

The office of *Tuesday's Child* underground newspaper was a tiny room filled with two mattresses, a typewriter and a pile of dirty clothes. I sat down beside a man with two toes missing and eyes pointing at different angles. He showed me a cartoon strip of black castles and witches. 'I'm trying to get a job doing these.'

The editor had long black hair and a shiny face. 'So you've been to the *Good Times*? We work a lot in collaboration with them. We've just given them our special interview with Charles Manson.'

'How did you get it?' I asked

'He rang us up and asked us to do it. Said he hadn't had one accurate interview. The next night, his telephone privileges were cut off.'

'What's he like?'

The editor smiled affectionately. 'He's very gentle. He can't go into the business of the murder, of course. That'd hurt him more than it would help him.'

'What else?'

'Well, he's very involved with Alastair Crowley. His handwriting was analyzed and it showed a lot of cosmic influences.'

'I think Alastair Crowley's a bit mad,' I said. 'He said this idiotic thing about women being as the ape and the parrot.'

'This paper's also influenced by Alastair Crowley,' said the editor serenely. 'Have some popcorn.' He passed the bowl.

'What do you think of the Chicago trial?' Martin asked.

The editor shrugged. 'It was all rigged. The straight reporters were ceded in the jury box. A briefcase full of guns and heroin was planted on Abbie Hoffman when he was arrested. He can't even have his telephone number under his own name. It's under Jerry Applebaum.' He looked mysterious. 'Even *our* telephone's bugged. Would you like to listen?'

'Look,' said Martin, 'do you know what's involved in bugging a telephone? It's a very complicated business, besides being very expensive.' He started to explain.

The editor sat there smiling. 'What do you think of the business at the Stones concert in California?' he asked us.

'Do you mean when the bloke got killed by Hell's Angels? We met this guy who thought Mick Jagger was a revolutionary,' said Martin. 'Ridiculous.'

'Mick Jagger never made a plea for peace; John Lennon did,' said the editor pensively. 'After that concert there were some wonderful photos of Mick Jagger in fear which gave me a wonderful insight into Mick Jagger.'

'What really did happen at the concert?' I asked.

'Well, this guy had a gun and rushed at the stage shouting, "I'll kill Mick!" so Hell's Angels killed him and took away his gun.'

'We'd better go,' said Martin.

'Would you like some copies of the paper?' the editor asked me. 'This is a good issue.'

He shoved four copies into my arms. The front page said, in big letters, 'THE MORE YOU COME THE MORE YOU CAN.' I laughed politely.

'He's obviously got some weird thing going with Charles Manson,' said Martin, as we stood outside. 'He's mad about the guy. And all that about the telephone being bugged. Absurd.'

'Maybe it is bugged,' I said.

The other paper we had to see was the *Los Angeles Free Press*. It was in another part of town. There were at least ten people working there, in separate rooms.

The person in charge was Andy. He had a red fleck in one eye and a matching olive-green pullover and trousers. His hair was very short.

Martin asked him if he'd read the manifesto, 'Points of Rebellion', and launched into an explanation of why he, Martin, thought it a bad idea for revolutionaries to have guns.

Andy sat there looking scornful and amused. Occasionally he tried to interrupt. Once he said, 'Look, I'm trying to tell you how America works.'

The secretary, Sue-Sue, wore corduroy culottes and a grey jersey.

'I know someone in England called Sue-Sue,' Martin commented. 'Even there they think it's cute.'

'Decadence is everywhere,' said Andy.

He offered us some back copies and we went into a small room with Sue-Sue.

'This is a real office, isn't it?' said Martin. 'I should think you're making a profit here.'

'Yes. The editor never meant it to be like that. Like, now, he has this real nice house and everything. He isn't really capitalist and I know it worries him.'

Sue-Sue sat on a stool swinging her legs and looking distressed. Martin patted her on the head. This infuriated me.

'You're all right, though, aren't you?' he asked her patronizingly.

'Well, that was the first real office,' said Martin, once we were on the street. 'That guy we talked to was like an executive. They've really got something going there.'

Before taking the bus that night we had some food in the bus canteen. I ate mine very quickly.

'My, did you inhale that?' said the old man next to me.

'Really, it's awful the way no one pays any attention to the soldiers when they come back from Vietnam,' said Martin, referring to the young soldier who had slapped me on the bottom earlier that day.

Martin would not make love to me and this was beginning to undermine me. What was wrong with me? Occasionally he lay on top of me on a bed and moved about as though he couldn't help himself. More often, though, he murmured, 'You're too young', like a refrain, as though protecting me from himself.

One day, after returning from breakfast in a downtown diner in New Mexico, I burst into tears of frustration. I cried out to Martin that I had never wanted to be a girl anyway. I hated having to be so passive.

'You're not a girl, you're a woman,' said Martin gently.

If I was a woman, why wouldn't he make love to me?

He seemed to think he was sparing me, but his ignoring me was insulting. Every so often he would flirt with another woman, often someone older, making me feel that her experience of life was more valuable than my youth.

On the borders of Mexico, in El Paso, the land was hot and dry. We ended our bus journey there in the early morning. At the terminal was an old Indian begging for food.

'Give him something,' I said.

We found a hotel and went to sleep.

When I woke, white sunlight was coming through the windows. We walked through the outskirts of the town, to a laundromat. Across the burned grass was a disused railway line. We sat outside waiting. Martin was very still. His hair looked gold in the sun. There were bloody marks on the side of his face, where he had shaved over a spot.

'Look at this!' He had picked up a bit of green glass from a Coca-Cola bottle. 'Look at the shape of its shadow on these steps.'

I thought, I want to see things before I die.

'Go and get the clothes.'

I went inside and fished the clothes out, one by one, tying them in separate bundles.

That night we had supper in a Mexican restaurant with photographs of American film stars on the walls. The only other people in there were two boys, both about twenty, a fat one with a pink healthy face and a smaller, thinner pale one. The fat one came up to our table.

'Do you know where we can score here?'

'No. Sorry.'

We ended up eating with them.

I was opposite the smaller one. He had a thin pointed face and large blue eyes. He said they came from Fort Knox army base, not far away, and that they were absent without leave. He only had six weeks more before being out of the army for good.

'What will you do?' I asked.

He shrugged dispiritedly. 'I guess I'll hitch round getting different jobs. Maybe I'll go to Canada. My brother might come with me.'

The beer arrived and the fat boy started pouring it out vigorously. He told us he'd been to London. 'I hired this cab. Said to the driver, "Show me everything there is to see." It took three days. Buckingham Palace, Tower of London, Soho . . . he took me to his home . . . took me gambling. At the end I gave him three hundred pounds. He wouldn't take it. In the end he took fifty.'

'But how did you have all that money?' asked Martin, with his puritanical disapproval, which was beginning to get on my nerves.

'It was my grandfather's. He owns this factory, see. It makes the wiring behind the dashboard of Ford motor cars.'

The small, thin boy was now lying with his head on the table.

'Hey, is he ill?' said Martin.

'Nah, he's just stoned.'

'Do you think men are resentful when they come back from Vietnam?' Martin asked. 'I mean, do you think they do things like bombing police stations?'

The small one shook his head vehemently. 'When you come back from the war, you don't want any more violence . . . Please let's not talk about the war.'

He put his head on the table again.

'What were you doing before you were drafted?' I asked.

He looked up. 'I was in college, studying creative writing.'

'Really? Why don't you go back?'

He shook his head. 'No, I wouldn't like it now. I still write things, though. Maybe one day I'll write a novel.'

The fat boy looked embarrassed. 'I don't really go in for this reading stuff. I think people should enjoy themselves. He's probably my best friend, but I think he's too serious half the time.'

The small one took hold of my sleeve. 'The best time I had was when I lived in this commune. It was when I was AWOL. The girls were Sharon and Cherry. And the guys were Mike and George. We shared everything, clothes and all.'

'What happened?'

'We were sleeping in this condemned house, see. One night I was out late and when I got back, everyone had gone. They'd been turned out. They left a note saying to meet them in Albuquerque. I got there about a week later, but there was no sign.'

He closed his eyes. 'Man, I am so stoned!' He leaned his head against the wall.

The fat boy got up. 'We better be going. We should be back at the base by eleven.'

The small one was wearing patched velvet trousers.

'Those are nice,' I said.

'Sharon made them for me.'

I was still thinking about the boy on the bus to Houston a few days later. He had seemed to like me, and hadn't patronized me as Martin did. Martin was always making me feel guilty that I had more money than other people of my age, and was better off than he was.

At first, in Chicago, I hadn't even found Martin attractive, but now I was used to him. The fact that he wouldn't make love to me was driving me mad. He still insisted on separate bedrooms in each hotel we went to.

We arrived in Houston at one in the morning. Two black men in overalls were leaning against a drinks machine.

'Are you a soul sister?' asked one.

I gave him a tired smile.

Our hotel rooms cost eight dollars a night, but it was too late to look for another.

Soon after dawn I was woken by shouts and the noise of people running up and down the corridor outside my room. 'Let It Bleed' was being played very loudly on a record player. I discovered I had awful stomach pains so stayed in bed. The noise continued for another two hours. Then someone bashed on my door and ran away.

Martin, in an adjoining room, decided something had to be done. 'Can I speak to the manager please? . . . Look, I got here about two this morning and was woken at six by people rushing up and down the corridor and banging on my door. Could you do something? I mean, it's still going on.'

I could hear the manager's blurred voice. 'That must be the schoolkids from Alabama. They arrived yesterday and we've nowhere else to put them.'

'Isn't someone in charge?'

'I guess the teachers are on another floor. I'll come and see.'

He stood there, fumbling with his cuffs.

'Well, I don't see why I should pay for four hours' sleep,' said Martin. 'I mean, I put the "Don't disturb" notice on my door. Also, this lady's ill.'

The manager stood in silence. Then he brightened up. 'Tell you what. I'll put you in the wedding suite one night free of charge. How would that be? It's never been used.'

We followed him up the corridor, carrying our things. All the children had disappeared, except for one little black girl in a pink dress.

'Now look, try not to make so much noise all of you,'

said the manager half-heartedly. 'This lady's ill.'

The little girl lowered her eyes.

The wedding suite had two double bedrooms, a sitting-room, two bathrooms and two televisions. The bedspreads and curtains were snow-white.

'It's very nice,' I said.

The manager looked pleased. 'It's never been used,' he repeated. 'I've only just bought this hotel, see.'

'Are you making money?' Martin asked.

He shook his head mournfully. 'Most of the people who stay in hotels stay in more expensive ones than this. I wouldn't wish a recession on anybody, but it sure would do me some good.'

Martin went out looking for an underground newspaper. I switched on the TV and got into bed with the channel adjuster. The first programme was a panel game with couples called Fifi and Mike, Dan and Berry, Lee and Georgie. They had to guess how many lavatories there were on the new Panam jet. Another lady, from New Orleans, had to guess which couple was right. If she guessed correctly, she would get a free holiday in New York. Lee and Georgie were the ones who got closest. Lee was wearing a false ponytail. Unfortunately the lady from New Orleans pinned her hopes on Fifi and Mike.

The next question was 'What turns your husband on?'

Lee and Georgie won again. Lee said what turned her husband on were girls in black stockings.

I wondered if I should go out and buy a pair of black stockings and wear them that night in our wedding suite.

Martin had now begun calling himself the Love Object. I wasn't sure at first why this made me uncomfortable. I didn't understand how subtly it diminished me. Why wasn't I his Love Object? This was my first experience of love, or what I thought was love, and it was extremely painful and unpleasant.

Martin, however, seemed flattered about being my Love Object. Using this phrase, I realized later, was a way of acknowledging my attachment to him, but also making it clear that he didn't return it.

We were getting to the end of our trip. Martin was beginning to run out of money and I had to use the last of my traveller's cheques to pay for him as well. He kept saying, out of embarrassment, guilt and mock humour, 'Just keep on signing.' He said he would pay me back the money, later, in England.

At the bus terminal there was a long queue for the bus to Kentucky.

'I want to sit next to you,' I said to Martin.

The snow was thick on the motorway and all around were the bodies of wrecked cars. I twisted round and started asking the boy behind me about being in Vietnam. 'What sort of rations did you have? What's an example of your lunch box?'

'Well, let's see, a can of beans, a bar of chocolate, cookies, dried apricots. That's B category. That's when you're on the move.'

'Was anyone very cruel?'

'Yeah, they were. Like, once, I was in this truck. We had a prisoner with us. The guys began poking him, taking the piss out of him. I didn't like that. They get very on edge, you see.'

I had come to depend on Martin absolutely. In the mornings when I woke up I thought, what will happen when I wake up and he won't be there?

As the bus drove into New York many hours later, I was afraid. While we were waiting in the terminal for our bags, a drunk old man accosted me. I smiled and was about to answer when Martin turned on me furiously.

'You ought to know better than to talk to drunks.'

'Make sure he looks after you,' murmured the old man, and slouched off.

We went to a hotel just off Times Square. The next morning Martin sat on my bed while I rang the front desk to ask about shipping luggage to England. (I had left two suitcases at my cousin's flat in New York.) On the telephone I knew I was ineffectual.

'You sounded like a kid. Why can't you do it properly? Stupid cow.'

I was silent.

At last I said, 'I don't call you names.'

On the way down in the elevator he stroked my face.

That evening Martin was off to see an avant-garde film. I went to the Lincoln Center, to see a musical. My cousin had given me the ticket.

Afterwards I sat for a few moments by the fountain outside. It was lit up, so that the water was green and red. Above me the sky was completely black.

I took out a pencil and wrote on my programme: 'I love you. I meant to say it before. Please, please, don't leave me.'

Then I took a taxi back to the hotel.

Martin was lying in bed reading. He looked very small and thin. He had lost weight on the bus trip.

'What was the film like?'

'Bad. I didn't talk to anyone.'

'Your shirt's filthy, you know.'

'I know. It'll have to be thrown away.'

I put my knees against the bed and rocked it backwards and forwards. 'Hey, I'm not a child.'

He pulled me down to him and began kissing me. He was very gentle. He tasted like honey.

Suddenly he pushed me away. 'Go to bed.'

'You're just being silly.'

He looked sad. 'Maybe I am.'

He took two of my fingers and squeezed them, then he pulled me down to him and hugged me. I was sick with love for him. I wanted to cry out, 'I'll do anything you tell me, anything at all.'

In England I went straight to my grandmother's. I tried to write up my experiences of America, hoping to make it into a book. Every morning I sat in my mother's old schoolroom with my portable typewriter. But Janet, my grandmother's maid, kept coming in and out, and somehow this made me feel that what I was doing wasn't to be taken seriously.

As for my grandmother, she was determinedly anti-intellectual, although her house contained several rare editions of beautiful books, bought by her second husband. (She didn't look at them, but read Agatha Christie and Dick Francis.) My grandmother saw writers as a different breed which had nothing to do with her. One of her few experiences of an author was a woman who had been brought to stay with her in the 1930s, and had then written an account of the weekend in a magazine. My grandmother said that in the article this woman had complained that she had not been given 'even a lettuce' to take home.

'If I'd known she wanted a lettuce, I'd have taken her up to the garden and found her one,' said my grandmother.

My father also, although he loved books and had told me, when I had had bronchitis in Edinburgh, 'When you're alone, books can be your friends', did not encourage me in my writing. Instead, he talked admiringly about Maria Elena, the Chilean wife of an English member of his club, who had written a book about how wonderful it was living in the country with six children and four Labradors. Maria Elena was a 'beauty' and this was presumably why my father, usually a good literary critic, was prepared to suspend judgement. It was ridiculous. If Maria Elena had looked like Evie the Bespectacled Cod, my father would have rubbished her book at once.

The world of my parents felt alien to me after my trip round America, and Martin's constant harping on class and income – particularly his own lack of the latter – had made me uncomfortably aware of my own privilege. I felt I must break away. Although I had had several discussions with my mother before I went to America about my future – I had asked her, 'Do I have to earn money?' but had not received a satisfactory answer – I had not had any such discussions with my father. He had given up any idea of a salaried job years ago himself, and, apart from once suggesting that I should become a spy, did not seem particularly concerned about whether I worked or not. My mother had not put any pressure on him to work as she said he was exhausted after his long war and deserved to rest. My grandmother told me that, after he left Madrid, my father had wanted to become an MP, but my mother had dissuaded him because, she said, he was too highly strung and 'only saw things in black and white'.

As for my brother, I wanted him to go to America too and see what it was like. But he was leading the same sedentary life as before, sitting in Sheila's flat most of the day, reading, experimenting with different drugs and making endless cups of tea while she went to her art college.

The bedsit smelled of new paint and was on Earls Court Road. It cost five pounds per week. I missed Martin, who, when he returned from America, two weeks after me, had gone back to live near his mother in Somerset.

I missed him terribly. He had written me two letters. One was about his novel, which had now been refused by the publisher, as he had not attempted to improve it and had spent the advance travelling round America instead; the second letter was about Socialism and space, or Space, I wasn't sure which.

I tried to reply intelligently to this second letter by mentioning a man I had met on a bus in Kensington High Street. This man said he had left Mexico City because he couldn't bear the poverty there. 'What difference does it make if he's in England or Mexico if the people there are still poor?' I wrote to Martin.

On the floor of my bedsit was a copy of the *Times* which I had bought that morning. A reader had written in criticizing the youth of today for seeking 'transient pleasures'. What pleasures weren't transient? I wondered.

I looked at myself in the mirror. I thought I looked sixteen, although I was twenty. I never wore make-up and I had straight brown hair, not well cut.

In the room next to me lived an American nun who was a member of an order called Little Sisters of Loretto. She told me proudly that the Little Sisters had stormed the Dow Chemical Company in Washington as a protest against bombing in the

Vietnam War. The nun asked me if I played bridge and when I said no, she lent me copies of an American GI magazine called *Stars and Stripes*.

I couldn't settle now I was back in England. It was so dull. The sky seemed lower and there were more clouds than in the American sky.

I drifted round London going to meetings. At the same time I wrote up my experiences in America. (I sent an article to *Nova* magazine, about cults, but it was rejected.)

Most days I wore a scarlet Moroccan cape which made me feel secure, although it was ostentatious. Men shouted, 'Little Red Riding Hood' or 'Miss Batwoman' at me in the street.

One afternoon I went to Caxton Street for a preliminary lecture on meditation.

'What's the five pounds for?' I asked a lady in the lift.

'Spreading the word,' she answered mysteriously.

The lecturer looked like a clergyman on *Songs of Praise*. 'There is no need for suffering,' he told us.

'How about when you're hit by a car?' I asked.

He thought for a moment. 'That takes two people.'

'Well, what about those signs "Falling Rocks Ahead"? You could be hit by rocks if you were driving alone.'

He looked at me pityingly. 'You aren't ready for meditation.'

Cults seemed to be in. The next day I was stopped by a smiling oriental in the King's Road who asked if I would buy a copy of *Process* magazine. He explained that Process was an organization which would teach you to 'develop your mediumistic abilities and allow yourself to experience a wider vision and a deeper understanding'.

He invited me to come to the Process coffee shop. I declined.

That afternoon I came upon Hare Krishna chanters in Soho Square. I had seen these men with shaven heads and orange robes already, in Detroit and San Francisco.

One of the chanters came from the north of England. 'By the grace of Krishna I found the Krishna temple as soon as I came to London,' he told me. 'Your soul benefits every time you hear me say "Krishna" . . . Now, wouldn't you like to buy a copy of the *Godhead*?'

The magazine was 4/6. I didn't buy it.

I looked in the *Red Mole* magazine and went along to Red Lion Square to hear a man with bulging eyes lecturing on the Indo-Chinese front. I told two people standing beside me that I had just come back from America. Although one part of the meeting was about bringing over a student from Kent State University to speak in London – it was just after American police had shot students at Kent State – most of the audience seemed to prefer to gossip about the pub they had ended up in after the latest Trafalgar Square demonstration.

I thought nostalgically of the last meeting I had attended with Martin in Greenwich Village just before I had returned to England. It had included Abbie Hoffman (one of the defendants in the Chicago trial), Jerry Rubin (another defendant and author of *Do It*, a subversive guidebook on how to upset the System) and an assortment of Black Panthers.

I began to yearn for America and Americans.

I met two girls from San Francisco, carrying baskets of vegetables in Portobello Road.

'London's so peaceful,' said one.

'But there's nothing happening,' I said. 'I like to feel I'm in History.'

'Not much point being in History if you get killed,' said the other.

Although he had written, Martin had not rung me after returning from the States. In the Bistro Vino in Gloucester Road, over spaghetti Bolognese, I told Rose about our trip, explaining, 'I was crushed absolutely. I had no perspective.'

I added, 'And now I'm seeing everything through his eyes.'

To distance myself from Martin I wrote a list of things I found unattractive about him: he had (a) spots (b) pale white eyelashes (c) legs shorter than mine (d) slightly crooked face.

Martin came up to London and we had a meal in an Indian restaurant. He was dispirited and worried about money and seemed to have given up any idea of rewriting his novel or submitting it to another publisher.

When he went back to Somerset, I missed him. I started crying at night in my bedsit and blowing my nose on white lavatory paper. I thought of Martin all the time, picturing him in different situations. Here he was with long hair, fluffy and clean, the time he came into my hotel room in New York and stroked my face. Or here he was in the Indian restaurant last week. There he had shorter, greasy hair, his face was shiny and he had looked shy.

Why had I ever asked him to come to America? Stupid, stupid fool! I should have gone on my own. Now I was stuck. I was no longer free. All I did was wait for letters and pretend he was still with me.

I was invited to a party in Somerset. That weekend there was a newspaper item about hippies being chased off the cliffs by angry farmers in St Ives, Cornwall. I remembered the time I had taken LSD on the cliffs in Devon with Rose and my brother, and how the local fishermen had stared at us. Perhaps we had had a lucky escape.

The day after the party I drove to visit Martin in the town where he lived. Birds Eye chicken pie cartons lay all over his living-room floor. On a table were two open books, *The Charter-house of Parma* and *The Chubb Family*, by Mrs Henry de la Pasture. There was also a pamphlet entitled 'Womanpower', produced by the Fabian Society.

I left to go back to London after a few hours. Martin hummed, to make me think he didn't mind my going. As I drove off, I watched him walking through the rain under his umbrella, with a rather self-conscious gait. A little boy with dark hair was staring at me curiously. He must wonder, why's that lady crying while she's driving a car?, I thought.

I saw Martin several times that summer. On one of these visits I found some items in his bedroom. I wrote them down in my diary:

Item A: a painting of apples in a bowl on a damp canvas by Meriel James.

Item B: postcard to Martin from Meriel James from St Ives, saying, 'Wish you were here.'

Item C: note from Meriel James telling Martin to ring her.

Item D: letter from Martin to Meriel James, arranging to meet.

I knew that Meriel James, who lived a few streets away from Martin, was an older woman with children. Martin, somewhat apologetically, admitted that he was having an affair with her.

Even then I went down to Somerset again. Once we drove to Lyme Regis. We sat on the beach and I threw little pebbles at Martin's stomach. He was wearing a blue jersey covered with his own light-brown hairs. He stood up and tried to make stones skim for me across the water. We both knew he was showing off. I returned to London with a red plastic rose in the back of my car. Martin had shot it down for me at a fair.

A few days later I read about one of the American students who was killed at Kent State University. She had had a 'hope' book, in which she wrote a list of things she wanted to do in the future.

In August I found myself again walking to Martin's flat, passing lines of cabbages in gardens, and wild red poppies. That evening, as we heated blackberries on the stove, Martin kept repeating, 'It's no good. It's no good.'

The only movement in the room was the smoke from the saucepan, from the boiling blackberries. Later I walked back through the same streets to the station, crying.

On the train I started reading *The Planetarium* by Nathalie Sarraute. My brother had lent it to me.

'Complete fusion exists with no one, those are tales we read in novels – we all know that the greatest intimacy is constantly being traversed by silent flashes of cold clear-sightedness, of loneliness.'

My view was that Martin would probably never write a good

novel and never earn any money. The only person who really needed me was my brother.

Then I had this dream. I am in an aeroplane, flying over the west of America. We are mounting higher. The noise is unbearable – screaming in my ears. I think, it's all right; it's only that we're flying . . . and suddenly we are over Ohio and there is a great peace. I am lying down in the body of the aeroplane. As I wake up, it seems that it's Martin I am lying on.

David Again

It was a year since I had returned from America.

David, now a law student in Scotland, was down south for the spring holidays. He was sympathetic about my disappointment over Martin and didn't seem to get bored when I obsessed about him. I showed David some of my writing about America.

He sat in an armchair in my Earls Court room, turning the pages. I went out to the bathroom. When I came back, he was reading something else instead.

'Look, this is what you should be writing . . . This is real . . . "I love you. I meant to say it before. Please, please, don't leave me."'

After he had finished – it was what I had scribbled on my programme the night before I left New York, but never showed Martin – David looked directly at me. I realized for the first time that, despite his straight floppy hair, his schoolboy good looks and his awkward, rather stiff manner, he was capable of passionate feelings himself.

Meanwhile, Rose had a new boyfriend, Jake, whom she had met at Oxford. He had been in America at the same time as I had. He wanted to be a playwright and had already written a fringe play about the Weathermen, a group of young American revolutionaries who had gone 'underground' and who made bombs. I was jealous, both of Jake's literary achievement and of the fact that once again Rose seemed to be having a successful love affair.

In April David took me round Wales on the back of his motorbike. It kept breaking down because of something he called 'the electrics'. Early one morning we found ourselves halfway up a Welsh mountain watching the crowning scene in Roman Polanski's film of *Macbeth*. We were then asked to move by a member of the crew, as the motorbike was being filmed by mistake. Unfortunately 'the electrics' played up again, and David had to push the bike ignominiously for ten minutes down the mountain, with me following on foot.

I was rather bad-tempered with David in Wales, especially as it kept raining. As we lay in bed one morning in a farmhouse near Snowdonia, he asked me if I had ever really been in love with anybody.

I replied thoughtlessly that I had loved Martin. When we got back to London, he told me I had talked about Martin for most of the trip.

My father took me and David to the Claremont Club in London. High-powered gambling went on there. Here, as in Greece when I was thirteen, once again was a glimpse of my father's more sophisticated life. I did not feel at home in this environment and nor did David, though he was too polite to say so.

The three of us met in the hall of the club, before going into the dining-room. My father was wearing his red velvet smoking jacket. He told David, who was in an old tweed coat with leather patches on the elbows, 'Christ! You look like a polytechnic student!'

My father did not win any money that evening.

Rose was working temporarily at the biscuit counter in Harrods. I used to go and chat with her. Supervising her was Mr Mitchell. He had been there for many years, and had a full knowledge of the biscuits. He deplored the new use of super-market trolleys in the food halls, and, like my father, who occasionally went to Harrods himself, Mr Mitchell noted with disappointment the deterioration of the clientele.

With Mr Mitchell on the permanent staff was Miss Charming. She had fluffy hair and spiky eyelashes and was a practising spiritualist, always going to seances. She had an admirer whom she referred to as 'may frehnd', who bought her clothes and jewellery.

The third assistant, like Rose, was young and temporary. He

was a Jamaican boy called Rolf. When I said I wanted to visit Paris, Rolf gave me the name of a hotel and I went off there two days later, giving up my room in Earls Court for good.

I was rather alienated in the hotel Rolf had recommended. On the street outside strawberries were being sold. It was a working-class area of Paris. I sat in my room eating *fromage* frais and trying to write, once again, about my experiences in America. I was taller than most people outside the hotel and this made me feel conspicuous.

I emigrated to the Latin Quarter, where I moved round a series of cheap hotels, changing every few days. I lived mostly on bananas, *fromage frais*, cherries and *crêpes* I bought in the street. Remembering Martin's craze for the French novelist Michel Butor, I applied to do a summer course at the Sorbonne on the *nouveau roman*.

At the end of his university summer term David came to visit me in Paris on his motorbike. I wanted to finish my literature course. We agreed that he would ride the bike to Italy and I would meet him the next week in Rome. We would then go on to Greece.

It was Bastille Day. I found myself behaving badly with David. We wandered all round the city, trying to find the place where the celebrations were. I groused at him for inefficiency, berated him when he wanted to sit down and drink coffee and, when we finally arrived at the square where the fireworks were, I rushed towards some Americans in jeans, with bands round their heads. David pulled me back and made me stand with him.

I sulked, then the band started playing some Spanish music. Suddenly I was smiling. I hung on to his arm and afterwards made him rush again through the streets, saying I was longing to go to a party. I found some students I knew in a café, and bought them all glasses of *café liégeois* (coffee ice-creams with whipped cream) to celebrate Bastille Day. But that night in our hotel bedroom I was distant again.

David made me selfish, I told myself. It was his fault. Usually he tried to give me my own way. But even when he did, I still did not really know what I wanted. I told him that I was afraid of loneliness. I said, 'When I sit down to write, I feel I'm the only person in the world.'

He said he liked being alone, he loved to read history and archaeology. He thought a lot about the past; sometimes it even seemed to him that he had lived before.

'Do you think I've got talent?' I asked him one day, in our hotel room, turning to him from my typewriter.

'Yes, no, I don't know,' he replied, rubbing his face with his hands.

He had avidly read Balzac, Zola and Stendhal. I imagined him as a middle-aged man, a solicitor, living in a farmhouse in Dorset with old-fashioned roses in its garden. He would know the names of butterflies and in the evenings he would sip a whisky and listen to classical music. He would look dignified, and have stooping shoulders. He would be one of those older men who always opened doors for women. A gentleman, in fact.

It wasn't only me who took advantage of David. When I arrived at Rome Airport, he told me of his journey over the French and Italian Alps, how he had given an American girl a lift on his bike and gallantly given her his sleeping-bag when they had to spend the night unexpectedly on a freezing mountain pass. Once in Rome the girl had ditched him, without paying him her share of the petrol money.

We drove to Naples. As we queued outside the youth hostel, I discovered I had left my passport in Rome. I went back at once to fetch it, then went by train to Brindisi, to where David had now ridden the bike in preparation for our ferry to Greece. I arrived at Brindisi after midnight, with two American girls whom I met on the train.

At the station we were accosted by six Italian boys, then supposedly rescued by a taxi driver who took us to a park just outside the town, where he said we could sleep in peace, as all the small hotels were full. We lay in our sleeping-bags near some bushes. Soon there was a commotion and a group of Italian boys, perhaps the ones from the station – we couldn't be sure – appeared from behind the trees, carrying flaming torches. They continued to annoy us all night, going away then returning, sometimes roughly poking us, one even tearing my shirt.

Around breakfast time, when they had finally gone, I walked down to the main road and hitched a lift with a grocer's van towards the town. We had only been going a few minutes when I saw David on his motorbike, so I shouted to the grocer to stop.

That afternoon, after we had bought our ferry tickets to Greece, the motorbike was stolen off the quay. It was recovered by the Italian police just as the boat was about to leave. David decided to leave it behind as it had been such a nuisance.

Why wasn't I satisfied with David as a boyfriend? He wasn't brutal, or sexy enough, for me. Other women wanted him, in particular Hailey, an American woman in her forties, whom we met in Santoríni. Hailey was travelling with her ex-lover, her son and a girl from a children's home in Boston, whom she had adopted for the summer. She and her lover had quarrelled, but had to stay together because they were writing a joint travel book on Greece. The adopted fifteen-year-old girl had just become pregnant by Hailey's son. Hailey confided her troubles loudly to David in various *tavernas*. He always had a sympathetic ear.

'She only wants to seduce you!' I hissed.

We were at that moment on one of the beaches, just before lunch.

'David! David! Come over here! I want you to help wash my bikini!' Hailey called out.

'You fool! That's just an excuse,' I whispered, as David started wandering towards her through the shallow water. 'She just wants to take her clothes off in front of you.'

David refused ever to believe that she had any ulterior motive.

We were staying in a room with two French students, charming blond Frédérique and his girlfriend, Anne. Frédérique spent most of his time in the room naked, singing a song by the

Beatles . . . 'finally took a train into Paris, honeymooning down by the Seine' . . . One evening he began whispering to David about an affair he'd had with an older woman in Paris. *'Mon Dieu*, old boy, it was like a Roman Polanski film!' But later, when he got stomach-ache, he moaned his girlfriend's name – 'Anne! Anne!' – throughout the night, like a little boy. He and Anne planned to open their own restaurant in Paris when they had finished university.

Towards the middle of August David had to set off back to England. I was going to stay on my own on the island for a week longer. But, as David's boat was about to depart, I took fright. A middle-aged schoolteacher from Harrow whom we had met in a taverna had taken a fancy to me. He insisted on calling me Elsie, and kept repeating, 'You're a cut above the other girls, Elsie!'

As I accompanied David down to the quay to say goodbye, I saw the schoolteacher on the hilltop above the port, waving his arms excitedly. I was now terrified of being left alone on the island with him in my persona as Elsie, so I rushed back to the village and collected my clothes, just in time to leave on the boat with David.

In Athens David wanted to stay overnight in the same hostel where we'd stayed on our journey out, although we had both thought it was horrible.

'You're like a homing pigeon!' I told him contemptuously. 'You only want the familiar. You're scared of anything new.'

Later, in our bedroom, I asked him, 'Do you think I'm too fat?'

'You're my Venus,' David replied.

I pretended not to hear.

David continued weaving in and out of my life, for years afterwards, like a piece of beautiful gold thread which I failed to pick up, preferring gaudier material.

Peter

I became Peter's mistress on a double bed in a damp room in
the East End. Some Irishmen had lived in the room before that.
The walls were covered with cracked Victorian wallpaper – a
pattern of gold and brown flowers. The corners of the room
leaned inwards, like the corners of a damp cardboard box. In
the yard a tree, otherwise bare, was littered with sparrows.

Although afterwards I wrote a banal entry in my diary –
'Peter and I made love; it was very good' – I soon realized that,
although he had lived in my house in Hackney for two months,
I knew little about him. Other men confided in me, but he had
told me nothing about the hospital where he was a medical
student or what he did for the Communist Party, and nor did
he mention his other, or former, girlfriends.

It was Peter's energy that I liked. He wasn't conventionally
handsome. He had red hair and narrow pale-blue eyes which
sometimes used to glitter in a diabolical way. (Or did I find it
more exciting to *think* he was diabolical?)

Peter was slightly shorter than I was. Unlike me, he seemed
to have no trouble telling others what to do. He easily gave
orders to the members of the commune which he had set up in
my house. However, the house in Hackney was mine – my
grandmother had paid for it, with twelve thousand pounds,
when I was twenty-one – and ultimately I had to take responsibility. I hated being a landlord and wished I was still in
Paris. My friend Rose, also now my lodger, had refused to fall
in with Peter's wishes that we pool our money, since, after
graduating from Oxford, she had now started her first proper
job, with a publisher. I thought that Peter's friend Fred and
Fred's sister, Nancy, who *were* members of the commune,
resented me for owning the house.

Even my former friend Rose, now that she was a lodger, seemed to have become an enemy. She didn't clean the bath or wash up and she kept the Hoover permanently in her room. Instead of buying Kleenex to blow her nose, she used up all the lavatory paper. She kept borrowing my clothes, and left her own dirty clothes permanently on the bathroom floor. She had also told her mother to use my house as a base whenever she came to London.

I got glandular fever and went to my grandmother's. Fred and Nancy left – she went to live in a bedsit with Jacques – and just Peter and Rose were in my house. They seemed very intimate and when I returned I felt excluded. I still felt weak. As I lay alone in my attic room, I thought I could hear secret comings and goings. I became convinced that Peter and Rose were having an affair. It was only then that I realized how much I was attracted to Peter.

One afternoon in November I lay in bed staring at the white London sky through the skylight. Seagulls, from the nearby canal, floated in it like bits of fluff. The back of my neck ached and my bedroom was full of dust. (Bullied by Rose, I had briefly employed a local cleaner called Mrs Plummer, but she had left after I had disclosed that I wasn't going to buy any fitted carpets.) I shut my eyes and tried to force my mind along practical channels. I formed a mental list of domestic chores, to try to persuade myself to lead a normal life, like other house-holders did.

'Washing to launderette. Ring gas man about mending storage heaters.'

But my mind wouldn't focus. I watched the sky change from white to navy blue to black. From where I was lying it wasn't clear if the lights ahead of me were other windows or stars. I felt as if I were grafted on to the night sky. I was slipping backwards into death.

I wanted to have an affair with Peter. But I did not know how to go about it.

A few days later, when we were on our own, Rose told me it

wasn't Peter she was involved with, but a young American woman called Sandy Streep. Sandy was living up the road in another commune, full of university graduates like herself. Rose had thought I might be annoyed about Sandy 'sleeping over' several nights a week so they hadn't told me. Peter, said Rose, seemed excited by the women's romance going on in the house.

I felt left out, confused and out of control. I typed an analysis of the situation, mainly for myself, and a list of rules, to try to impose some order. At twenty-one, I did not want to own and run a house.

The next day Peter told me that he was going to leave and move in with Fred, who was now living in a small flat in Bethnal Green. Peter wanted to be more involved in the lives of his patients at the East End hospital where he was training, he explained. He called them 'my old ladies'.

This phrase, his 'old ladies', made me feel slightly uncomfortable. Wasn't it a bit patronizing? I didn't feel, however, that I was in a position to judge. A few days after he moved out Peter and I began our own affair, in the flat in Bethnal Green which he now shared with Fred, and in my own attic room, where we made love to an old Elvis Presley LP that I'd bought in a shop off New North Road.

Besides studying to be a doctor, Peter had also started a radical newsletter about medicine, of which he was the editor. He was busy and made me feel there were more important things in his life than me. I found this, and the disciplined rhythm of his life, reassuring.

One morning when I went round to the flat I found a girl psychology student with long black hair on his floor in a sleeping-bag. She had a mouth curling up at the ends and narrow, very green eyes. She talked in a serious and emphatic voice about China and People's Power. She made me feel inadequate and I thought she despised me for not earning my living.

I had now given up a job I had had as a publisher's reader and was living on money I had inherited from my grandmother when I was twenty-one. This irritated and confused Peter, who was a Marxist.

'I don't approve of your lifestyle,' he declared. 'I see life as a struggle. There are so many things that need doing. You're frittering your life away.'

I wasn't working for three reasons. One was laziness. Two was that I didn't yet need the money. The third reason was that I wanted to be a writer. Whenever I took on a job, I realized that the only effort I really wanted to make was with my own writing. It was difficult to justify this to Peter, since I had never had anything published. He thought I ought to do a job as well.

Our situations were different. I had a car and he was still living on a student grant, which meant he had to eat omelettes and potatoes, and stay in his section of London most of the time as he couldn't spend money on tube fares.

At the beginning of the affair I rather took him for granted. Sometimes he would ask, 'Do you love me?'

I never said yes, because I wasn't sure if I did. During our love-making my mind was often separated from my body. Perhaps I detached myself from things that might hurt me. One night he had toothache. He said, 'I don't want to be wet or anything.'

I longed to say, 'You're so sweet, darling. I love you so much.' But, as my father had once said, I was undemonstrative.

Peter sometimes used to ask, 'Do you think I'm handsome?'

I didn't answer because I didn't think he was, though I found him sexy.

By now I had another lodger. Rose had moved out, as she wanted to live with Sandy. I had begun to like Sandy and thought she looked sweet in her habitual pink dungarees. She told me to occupy myself by going round 'consciousness-raising' on the local housing estate. I thought if it was full of women like Mrs Plummer, this wouldn't be very popular.

My new lodger, Elizabeth, like Peter, was very keen for me to work.

'You'd be perfectly capable of sitting down from nine to five every day,' she said sternly.

I thought this was probably true.

I went to an agency in Fleet Street. It was called the Arthur Carr agency and was supposed to be for those who didn't fit in. Previously I had applied to Graduate Girls agency, which had got Rose *her* job, in publishing, but they had not liked my written CV – university drop-out, secretary in New York, sorter of hospital linen, aspiring novelist, publisher's reader, assistant collector of underground newspapers.

'It would have been much better if you hadn't had any jobs at all than all these different ones,' I was told by the head of Graduate Girls.

I had thought the different jobs made me sound versatile. But I wasn't a graduate girl anyway, as I had never graduated, so probably I shouldn't have gone there in the first place.

The Arthur Carr agency had found me an interview with a publisher. Elizabeth came with me on the bus for part of the journey.

'Now for goodness' sake, make them think you're the only person in the whole world they want to employ,' Elizabeth advised as we sat side by side. 'And put on some lipstick. And pull your skirt up. Men like leg.'

I thought I knew just as well as Elizabeth what men liked. However, I had not used lipstick for two years.

'I think I'd rather not wear lipstick,' I said. I already felt insecure because I was smartly dressed.

Elizabeth herself was glamorous, in a formal style which did not appeal to me. She had just bought a navy and white suit to wear at women's press conferences. She was a journalist on the fashion page of a newspaper. I thought her skirt was like a tennis skirt.

'Goodbye, see you in two days,' said Elizabeth, springing lightly off the bus. It was Friday and she was going to spend the weekend with her Catholic aunt after she finished work.

Too late, I noticed she had left her make-up bag on the seat. Perhaps there would be some make-up in it I could use to impress my potential employer. I might change my mind about lipstick.

I opened it. The first thing I saw was Bidex Female Deodorant. Next was 'Frador. Red liquid for mouth ulcers. Do not spill.'

The man in the seat opposite looked at me oddly. I managed to get out some lipstick called Plum Peach. But how could I put it on without a mirror? I decided to wait till I found a public lavatory.

'You must get a job, *any* job,' Elizabeth had advised. 'You're frittering your life away.'

She had used exactly the same words as Peter. I thought she was frittering her life away by sitting in an office every day rewriting pieces about dresses in Debenhams. I thought that my own life was more interesting. It was irresponsible and uncommitted. If there was a meeting, I went to it. So far I had been to a radical lawyers' discussion in a pub in Camden Town, an anti-internment meeting in Hammersmith, a talk on scientology, a gathering of Trotskyists in Maidavale and a Gay Liberation Seminar. I never actually took much part.

Peter disapproved of this.

'Why do you think these conferences are organized? You're supposed to get involved in what's going on,' he said.

He had threatened to abandon me if I went on drifting. I realized it was blackmail, but decided to submit to it.

'I see life as a struggle. There are such a lot of things to be done,' he had said again. 'You'll only be happy helping other people.'

So here I was, not exactly helping others, but on the 171 bus, all dressed up for a publisher's interview.

In Soho it was still early. The publisher's office was at the north end of Soho. Mr Stenhouse, who interviewed me, had a blond moustache. When I said I had written half a novel, he said that publishers were often failed writers.

'Maybe I'm too young to be a failed writer yet,' I said.

We talked about some characters from the London 'underground scene', whom my brother and I had met. We also talked about America, where Mr Stenhouse said he usually went for six weeks a year.

'I'd like to go back there,' I said.

He said he was 'full of anguish' for the American people.

'Yes, but it's a drama unfolding,' I said importantly.

I talked about two of the newspapers Martin and I had visited, the *Seed* in Chicago and the *Good Times* in San Francisco.

The publisher asked me if I was from a literary family. I said unfairly, 'No, my parents are Philistines.'

He told me that he was looking for a new permanent assistant, and that usually the only reason one of his staff left was to get married.

'Can't have any disruptive influences,' he said.

(I had stupidly told him I was tempted to go to India on a bus organized by a man called Mr Latif, whose name I had seen on a noticeboard in Earls Court and with whom I had had a meeting in a pub near Victoria Station. 'Bus get stuck, boy sleep with girl! Great fun!' Mr Latif had said, describing his bus experience of the previous year.)

I did not hear from Mr Stenhouse or the Arthur Carr agency. After three days I rang the agency. The lady who took my call said, 'Because of your odd voice, Mr Stenhouse assumed you were on drugs.'

(I knew from occasionally hearing my voice on tape that it was sing-song and had odd intonations. I had once been told by an ENT specialist, whom I had seen for my bronchitis, that I was not using certain vocal cords and that if I wanted to change my voice, I would have to have intensive speech therapy.)

After this failure I decided to go for a more radical job. I went and volunteered to work at the North Kensington Law Centre. It was the first law centre in London. I wanted to please Peter, but I was also interested in how the law was applied to those who were badly off. To get involved in a law centre was surely more balanced than joining the Communist Party?

Peter seemed content with my new activity. It also meant that I became more independent, partly because the law centre was the other side of London, some distance from where he and I lived.

When I did see him, he often said I interfered with his work. I realized that he couldn't control me, as he did his other contemporaries, who were willing to be dominated. (I thought that he had deliberately chosen friends who were subservient.) He was dependent on the goodwill of certain female medical students who were prepared to be docile around him, which I wasn't. One of these was Harriet, a stolid, sensible girl with a gruff voice who, like him, was a student at the London hospital. Harriet was always available to type out material for his newsletter. I did not fit into his life in the neat way she did. He did not know how to deal with me, because I did unexpected things, like turning up late at night without warning. Sometimes he scolded me. One night he said he was shocked that I never had anything in the fridge. I burst into tears and said I did not know how to run a house as I had had no one to copy. My mother had hardly ever set foot in her own kitchen.

One night in February Peter proposed to me in a Soho pub called The Intrepid Fox. It was during the miners' strike. Electricity was short all over London so there was a blackout. The alcoves of The Intrepid Fox were littered with embracing bodies. We had been to two pubs already. The flickering candles made the interiors look as though they had gone back a hundred years.

Peter emptied his glass of Guinness.

'What do you want most in life?' he asked.

I thought for a while bashfully. Then I shook my head.

'I'll tell you. You want to get married. Why don't you marry me?'

'What does it entail?'

Peter looked determined. 'It means you have to cook my meals and encourage me in my work. It means you'll have to sacrifice some things, but then do others in more depth.'

'Well, I can't think of anyone else,' I admitted.

Did this mean I had accepted, we both wondered.

Without telling Peter, two days later I set off on a skiing holiday in Poland with a group of acting students. On the train journey from Warsaw to the mountains I longed to be with Peter. Why wasn't I with him, instead of on a train in Poland? Perhaps I felt safer on my own. When I returned, nothing more was said about Peter's marriage proposal, and I even wondered if I had heard him correctly that night in the pub.

Our affair continued, rather half-heartedly. Often Peter was too busy to see me. Partly to please him, and partly out of curiosity, I attended the Communist University that summer. Run by the Communist Party of Great Britain, nearly every year it was held in the buildings of London University, near Tottenham Court Road and Goodge Street. Peter was helping with the administration. Much of the time he sat at a desk in the main hall while I went to lectures. I had chosen history as one of my subjects.

Peter had asked me to put up two students, Gary and Vince, who'd come to London specially to attend the Communist University. Gary, from Surrey, was very serious.

One teatime, after his lecture on education, I heard him coming in the front door. I shouted, 'Gary! Gary!'

He had curly black hair and glasses. He came and sat on my bed, which was a mattress on the floor. (I had taken over Rose's old room on the ground floor.) I was reading the *Morning Star*.

'I think this is a most awful paper,' I said.

'Oh,' said Gary, in a very disappointed tone.

'Look at this editorial about the strike,' I said. 'Complete oversimplification. Listen to this: "The working class will not tolerate the introduction of a police state in Britain." First, is there a police state? Second, if there is, not only the working class will not recognize it.'

Gary looked pitying. 'You should order the *Morning Star* every day,' he said. 'Which paper do you read?'

'The *Guardian*,' I replied. 'Have you ever read *Soviet Weekly*?'

'Yes, I have,' said Gary. 'It tells you what cultural activities are going on, art, folk dancing, things like that.'

'To try to make the capitalist world think art's really allowed to go on there, I suppose,' I said.

Gary looked very shocked by this cynicism.

I preferred Vince, who was from Strathclyde, where hundreds of men had just been made redundant in the shipyards. Vince seemed to have come to London mainly for a good time. He drank a huge number of pints of beer and checked the football results every day. He laughed a great deal, but looked as if he hadn't had enough to eat.

Peter continued to educate me in the ways of socialism. One evening during my stint at the Communist University he took me to a play in a north London pub called *Waiting for Lefty*, which was about a taxi drivers' strike in New York. It included scenes in which a young doctor, like Peter himself, proclaimed himself disgusted by the health situation in his own country.

Every so often the actors ran up and down among members of the audience shouting, 'Strike!'

I thought the play would have been more effective if it had been performed in a factory among men who were about to strike and needed a final push towards it. As it was, the audience consisted of three American tourists and a number of students from the Communist University.

Afterwards the students went to the bar and drank pints of bitter and discussed Marxism.

I went into the pub garden. Peter joined me.

'What did you think of the play?' he asked me.

'I thought that a scene in the French play *1789*, which I saw in a barn in Vincennes last summer, was better. The women in that play saying, "We have no bread" was more effective than the American woman in *Waiting for Lefty* saying that her child had never tasted grapefruit,' I told him.

Peter looked very scathing. 'One can't be bothered with the niceties of production when there's a message to be got across,' he said.

'But if you follow that argument to its logical conclusion, there's no need to bother even to dress up the actors or be on stage at all,' I pointed out.

Peter didn't answer. Sometimes I was afraid he thought me beneath any serious discussion.

'Well, I must go and talk to the boys,' he said.

I stood looking over the pub wall into the dark. I realized that, unlike most of my friends, Peter did not enjoy his conversations with me. Was it for this perverse reason that he was my lover?

As the Communist University went on, I saw more and more that I did not really understand Peter. It was not in my nature to have an *idée fixe*. His idea of Communism seemed to me narrow and blind; he drew lines between 'the new world' and 'the old world', without appearing to have much experience of either. When he got a postcard from sturdy old Harriet, who had chosen, for her holiday, to cut sugar cane in Cuba, I commented on the loveliness of the scene on her postcard.

'It's a paradise,' I said.

'It's a *socialist* paradise,' he corrected me.

Surely this was absurd? The sand would have been there, so would the sea, even if the Nazis had been in power.

Yet Peter had a certain charisma, by virtue of the very stubbornness of his ideals. I remembered how, when he and his friends had first moved into my house in Hackney, there had been no furniture. He had started a fire in the grate and sat in front of it working, his acolytes around him. Another communist paradise.

Two days after the Communist University ended I lay in the morning sun, in the dust, under a draught. On my right, through the open window, I could see the white flimsy curtains of the house opposite, where Peter's local grocer was still asleep with his wife. Their curtains had different kinds of lace patterns, one of clover leaves, one of daisies and one of diamonds. The grocer's shop was underneath. The grocer was called Mr Jones.

Turning over on my mattress, which was scuffed with dirt, I watched Peter asleep, in a bed on the other side of the room. He looked very strong, like an animal, I thought. I could see the hair on his face. I imagined how he would be in twenty years. I felt awed, almost afraid, because he was my lover.

My father, although he did not meet Peter, was surprisingly tolerant about his communist views. My mother, obsessed with Russia, both White and modern, was anti-communist. She had been there twice with my father and five or six times without him. To her excitement she had even been mistaken for a Russian in a side street of Moscow – she had broken away from the group and gone off exploring on her own – presumably because of her high Slavic cheekbones.

Once, in the middle of my stint at the Communist University, my father took me and my mother to an expensive French restaurant near Sloane Square where he had ordered caviare, and we began a discussion about communism. I said dramatically that probably in a few years most of the world would be communist. My father, displaying a sense of fairness which was one of his most agreeable characteristics, said that there was 'definitely a case for it'.

During the meal my father started pontificating about modern young women, saying that they couldn't expect to get anywhere because 'they opened their legs far too easily'.

'Why shouldn't women enjoy sex as much as men?' I asked him angrily.

My father, seeing the justice of this, fell silent.

Rose, who had now split up with Sandy Streep, sent me to a psychoanalyst called Peggie. I had broken up with Peter and was distressed.

Peggie was a former pupil of Jung and had curly white hair. The second time I saw her she looked abnormally red in the face, as though she'd been too much in the sun. I couldn't think of much to say to her.

On this visit I started explaining to Peggie about her solicitor, who was a Mr Loup pronounced 'Loo'. 'I rang my mother and she said it was better not to change to Mr Loup,' I said. 'She told me it was better to stick to my family solicitor.'

'I see, dear,' said Peggie. 'Well, that's all right. Only you seemed so confused about your material world when you first came in that I thought I'd better organize something.'

'You were right,' I said. 'I was very confused. But it was about my ex-boyfriend, not my material world. I was shaken up by the end of my affair. That's why I came to you.'

'How is your ex-boyfriend?' asked Peggie. 'Have you had a dream since I last saw you?'

'No. I already told you about that peculiar dream with me at a cocktail party in a wheelchair, didn't I? About me giving my father a barley sugar?'

'Ah yes. We decided it meant you had lost your standpoint,' said Peggie.

'Well, since then I haven't actually had a dream,' I said. 'One night, though, something very odd happened. I was about to ring a new possible boyfriend when a nightmare image of my former boyfriend beheaded rose before me.'

'My goodness!' said Peggie. 'Well, you know, we Jungians say that the head means an idea. Perhaps it means that you were getting too intellectual.'

'No, it meant I was about to take another lover,' I said. 'It was a warning not to.'

I had parted from Peter one Saturday, at a party in Kennington. I couldn't stand any more emotion. I was burned up inside. Quite suddenly at the party he seemed to wilt. He wandered round looking for Harriet, his dependable medical student. I couldn't reach him, because he didn't trust me.

'My darling,' I wrote the next morning, 'I need you. It is more a need than a love. Or both. I suppose they are the same.'

I wrote this in my diary, not to Peter himself.

In any case, he had left the party with solid old Harriet.

At breakfast I was suddenly overcome with dreadful nausea. My new lodger, Rick, padded about the kitchen like a Chinaman. He had straight silvery hair and narrow eyes, and wore a silk kimono.

'I feel like the girl in that poem by Lord Tennyson,' I said, looking at my half-eaten boiled egg. 'You know, the one which goes:

> She only said, "My life is dreary,
>   He cometh not," she said;
> She said, "I am aweary, aweary,
>   I would that I were dead!"'

Rick looked confused. 'Is there a paper?' he asked.

'Yes, there is, but I've taken it upstairs.'

Rick went and sat on the sofa and began the *Guardian* of three days earlier. I went upstairs and cleaned my teeth for the third time. I noticed that my lips were covered with white spots. They must be due to either worry or too much bacon.

I had dreamed about Peter again. I dreamed he had fallen in love with a communist girl. In the mornings now, when I woke up, I wanted to get back into the dark. I wanted to lie in a red room with shutters for a long time, and wake up very slowly. I wanted to creep into the cave of sleep.

Or I wanted to be in a room with walls, in the dark. Or in a room with walls made of books. I had heard about a woman who had started a bookshop because she couldn't have children.

When I used to wake with Peter, it was as though the sun had burst into the room. I associated him with the sun, perhaps because he had red hair. When I was sleeping with him, I had felt powerful.

Tim, a boy whom I had met in Rose's room at Oxford when I had visited her there, rang me. (He had written me a wistful letter, inviting me to a performance of *Hair*, which I had seen already.) He was pale and soft-skinned, with gold hair.

'Do you like life?' he asked in the kitchen the next day.

He made me feel sad.

'You've got deadness of the spirit,' I said to him.

When I was with him, I felt that we were in an enclosed world of the brain. I was unable to do normal things, like point out buildings to him. He didn't seem to notice the outside world.

Rose said, 'He's too cold-blooded for you.'

Tim told me, 'Sex is cerebral with me. Is it with you?'

'What does "cerebral" mean?'

'Of the mind.'

When I told Rose, she said, 'But sex isn't cerebral with you.'

My mother, who had met Tim's parents, and had a yen for blonds, found Tim attractive.

'Your mother practically gets an orgasm every time she sees Tim,' my father commented. 'He's not going to get much of an income writing the occasional article for the *Spectator*, is he?' he pointed out.

I knew that ultimately Tim wanted a conventional wife or girlfriend and, although kind-hearted, was snobbish. He also wanted to do things that cost money, like skiing every year or learning to fly. I sensed that he was jealous I had more money than he did. Although he had a degree in modern languages, he had not yet decided on a career.

Anyway, I was still hankering after Peter and regretting the end of our affair, which we had never even discussed. Tim decided to go on a long trip to the Middle East, where he could teach English as a foreign language. He rang to say goodbye and commiserate because I had flu.

My affair with Peter was now really over. My brother, trying to comfort me, jokingly offered to go round to his flat and horsewhip him.

My father took me to lunch at the Ritz. As usual, there were long silences, except when my father burst out with abrupt comments, usually about someone he recognized: 'There's old Monkey Hawkins. His mother's black as your hat.' Or: 'The reason your cousin Fee-Fee is so peculiar is that her husband, that nauseating old Mickey, could never get it up. He told Dick Lancaster one day in the club.'

Although my father did not refer to my own broken love affair, he suddenly started talking about his cousin, who, he said, had been jilted at the age of twenty-one by a young army subaltern. He then broke off, to watch an elegant blonde woman, in a pale-green silk suit, enter the dining-room. He observed, 'I wouldn't mind doing spermia with her.'

As we drank our coffee, my father remarked, 'You should give away some of that money your grandmother left you. Give it to charity.'

He then reminded me that I owed him the two pounds I had borrowed from him the week before.

Andrew

It was horrible to kiss them; their make-up was so glaring. Douglas, who seemed to be the leader of the three, and also the most feminine, wore gold eyeshadow, a dress with frills and gold lamé stockings. He had hennaed hair. My friend, Andrew, wore a black sleeveless dress and red stilettos. He was awkward in them, I thought. He looked softer in his ordinary day clothes – blue denim dungarees, T-shirt and a simple badge saying 'Gay Liberation Front'.

In these out-of-date women's clothes which he was wearing tonight, at my party in Hackney, he appeared more aggressive than he really was. He confessed that he would like to dress up as Margaret Rutherford and wander through Selfridges. It seemed a harmless enough ambition.

I had met him in King Edward's Hospital for Officers while I was having my wisdom teeth out. A friend had brought him to visit me. On that occasion he had not been wearing women's clothes, but the blue dungarees. However, he had left his red stiletto heels in a bag beside my bed by mistake, thereby demonstrating perhaps, unconsciously, how uncomfortable he found them.

Andrew had just 'come out'. He was in his thirties and had been a successful financial journalist, on the *Times*. Now he had joined the Gay Liberation Movement, which had started in America, and decided to change his life.

The *Times* had refused to publish an article by him about Gay Liberation. As part of his 'coming out', Andrew had paraded in his father's club wearing women's clothes. The *Spectator*, run by George Gale, had then published his article that the *Times* had rejected.

Andrew had also appeared on a television programme and

talked about being homosexual. (As a result a childhood friend of his said he was so shocked he could have nothing more to do with him.)

Shortly after my party Andrew went to live in a commune in Bethnal Green Road with several other gay men and women. It had formerly been the Agit-Prop bookshop. The new occupants named it Bethnal Rouge. Under the flat where the commune members lived was the new bookshop, now selling books mostly about gay subjects. Unfortunately some members of the commune were more interested in drugs than in selling the books.

I fell momentarily in love with Andrew that day when he entered my hospital room. I fell in love with his gentleness, and his violet eyes with their long black lashes. Also, he was the first homosexual I had met who seemed to like women. He liked me. I loved his self-deprecating humour, his sweetness and his courage. By nature he was retiring; but, because of his convictions, he had chosen to expose himself to the public gaze. Only a few years before, until 1967, it had been an offence to have sex with a man. Andrew said that in those days the police had sometimes tried to frame him and his friends. Once he had been holding hands with a man in a car in Soho and two policemen had hauled them out and given them a hard time.

In court I was fined ten pounds for putting a franc inside a parking meter. (A plain-clothes policeman had popped up from behind a car. It emerged that he had been planted there by his boss, to watch out for people who had been feeding meters with inappropriate objects, such as the tops of beer cans.)

When I arrived at Marylebone Magistrates' Court, I found Andrew and several of his friends there. They were also on trial that afternoon, for wearing drag in a pub in Notting Hill Gate and causing a disturbance. Douglas was in a pink polka-dot dress and he had glitter round his eyes. Richard, another friend, wore an ankle-length black satin dress with matching pill-box hat and net veil; Andrew himself wore a dress patterned like a Persian carpet. Most of their Gay Lib supporters wore heavy turquoise and purple eye make-up and were very rude. After my own short trial was over I sat in the public gallery with them to watch. (The magistrate had laughed out loud when I had pointed out that a franc was worth more than five pence, but had fined me anyway.)

I noticed that some of those with me in the gallery smelled. A girl with red hair who had been behind me in the queue had watched me walk in, but then wasn't allowed in the gallery herself. Her friend, who had a mouth the colour of a mulberry and was already seated, was furious.

'She can't come in because of you.'

I said, 'Don't be silly. Three people just went out. She could have come in then.'

Why should Gay Lib occupy the whole public gallery anyway? I thought.

One of the men in the dock down below said, 'We like to be effeminate. Our way is non-violent.'

The magistrate said that Douglas, when he was arrested, was alleged to have remarked, 'I'm not doing what the working class tell me.'

The magistrate said that this was such an odd statement that perhaps the policeman had invented it, but then it was a very unusual remark for a policeman to make up, so surely Douglas must have said it after all.

I admired Andrew's calm and dignified manner when he gave his testimony, a contrast to his supporters upstairs in the gallery, who were told several times to be quiet by the magistrate. At least one of them shouted, 'Pigs!' at the police below.

Afterwards I had coffee with my solicitor in a café the other side of Marylebone Road. The Spanish waitress was laughing hysterically because some of the Gay Lib supporters had been in there earlier saying things like 'Where's my boyfriend?' and squirting scent all over the place.

I did not tell my father about my new friendship with Andrew. He called all homosexuals 'bugger-boys' and whenever he saw any would declare, just out of their hearing, 'Backs to the wall everyone!' Shortly after I met Andrew my father claimed that he had been 'goosed' in his local London pub, the Duke of Wellington, and he was furious about it. 'Leave my arse alone!' he had yelled in the crowded saloon bar.

My mother claimed that her homosexual cousins – one had been sent down from Oxford in the 1930s for wearing make-up – were petrified of my father and had decided that it was better for their nerves if they met him as infrequently as possible.

That Christmas I went home as usual. Andrew was staying about six miles away, with his parents, and I looked forward to going there for lunch on Boxing Day. I thought it would be more relaxing than our own family celebrations.

My father usually began Christmas by knocking several balls off the tree. It was in the hall outside his study. His dog, Raven, sometimes knocked a couple of balls off too, with his tail, as he followed my father. In the study, a room with very dark panelling, almost black, my father sat drinking whisky, looking in *The Oxford Dictionary of Quotations* for clues to the *Times* crossword, or flicking through his book of Charles Adams cartoons.

My father did not help with the preparations for Christmas, except, when we were children, he had lent two thick socks for our stockings and had helped my mother fill them at midnight. (My brother, aged five, had heard Father Christmas say 'Fuck' at the foot of his bed.)

Each year I, the only daughter, would help my mother unpack the boxes of Christmas decorations. They were in a locked room where my mother kept other treasures – her books on Russia, a donkey harness from a village in Spain and the birthday books belonging to me, Jonathan and Luke. (In my own birthday book was a four-leafed clover which I had found, aged three, on the common in Berkshire. My mother had proudly stuck this in, opposite a cutting of my hair.)

Among the boxes of Christmas-tree balls were six beautiful birds – peacocks – packed in cotton wool. I loved these birds. They were light blue, pink and green, and had white plumed tails.

My mother and I carefully attached them to the branches of the tree.

My mother also had a crib with wooden figures which she had bought when we lived in Spain. She arranged this every year on the hall table. The stable where the baby Jesus was born had a roof made of real straw. The faces of Our Lady and St Joseph looked grim and unsympathetic.

My father's self-appointed role at Christmas was to see that my brother and I went to Mass. This year my brother arrived on Christmas Eve at about midnight. We had only ever been to Midnight Mass once. We had arrived late and stood at the back. A man was sick behind us and I remembered hearing the splat as the sick hit the floor. The Christmas before this, when we had gone to morning Mass, my father had hit a car as we pulled on to the main road. He had thought that one of the nuns who was getting a lift with us had said, 'Go!' when really she had said, 'Whoa!'

'Bloody fool! Why didn't she say, "Stop" instead of "Whoa"?' said my father, during the post-mortem after the crash.

This Christmas I went alone with my father to morning Mass. (My brother, enraging my father, who suspected he was 'on drugs', refused to get out of bed. An hour before we were due to set off my father strode into my own bedroom and flung open my curtains, reverting to an unpleasant habit he had adopted when I was a teenager.)

The same parishioners were at Mass: Evie the Bespectacled Cod, Half-wit the doctor, and a woman my mother had made friends with, who had taught Luke French at primary school. My father did not show any interest in staying to wish them Happy Christmas, but charged out before the end as usual.

By the time we got home from Mass it was nearly mid-day. The lights of the Christmas tree had been turned on. As a child, I had wanted Christmas to be perfect but there was always something wrong. My father went straight into his study, slamming the door. On the way he knocked another ball off the tree and it broke. My mother laughed nervously and admiringly.

Such clumsiness was evidence of my father's masculinity. Either he raged through the house like a frustrated bull or retreated to his lair, his study. Why was he so unhappy? Every afternoon (except on Christmas Day, when he waited to hear the Queen's speech) he went to his bedroom soon after lunch. There was a strong smell of feet in there. My father lay for hours, his curtains drawn.

There were hardly any Christmas decorations in his study. A few bits of holly over the mantelpiece was all he wanted, or was given. On the mantelpiece, among the Christmas cards, was the birthday card I had sent him in French. It said: 'Je préfère les argentés.' When I bought it, I had thought the word 'argentés' meant 'silver-haired'. Now, when I looked at it again, I thought that probably the word meant 'moneyed'. Was the card therefore unintentionally a subtle insult to my father, as he wasn't rich? I had not meant it like that, and my father kept the card permanently on the mantelpiece, as a compliment to him from his only daughter.

Also on the mantelpiece were three framed photographs, one of Raven, his paws crossed, looking dignified, one of me between my parents at the dance I had had at my grandmother's, aged seventeen, pretending to enjoy myself and looking, I thought, idiotic, and a third photograph of one of the destroyers that my father had commanded during the war. (This was the ship that, after my father left it, had been torpedoed; most of the men had been drowned. My mother told me that my father had been devastated. He had written to the wives and mothers of the drowned sailors and many of them had written back, saying, 'If you had still been commanding the ship, it wouldn't have gone down.')

Lining the walls on one side were my father's collections of the novels of Evelyn Waugh, Graham Greene and H. H. Munro, or Saki. In another bookcase were his books of cartoons and a book of black and white photographs of Brigitte Bardot, mostly with few clothes on.

Christmas lunch. My mother had taken more decorations

out of her locked room, for the dining-room table. It looked very pretty. The centre decoration was a round cake made of cotton wool. On it was a tiny Father Christmas, a reindeer and minute Christmas trees and little red houses. The other table ornament was a pure white reindeer, a foot high, standing on its own.

Just before lunch my grandmother arrived, placid as ever, trying to pretend our family was normal. (My brother had finally got up, but had not brushed his hair and his jeans were filthy. He smelled, of unwashed clothes, drink and cigarettes.) At lunch my father was restless. He left the table before we pulled the crackers, going back to his study alone to wait for the Queen's speech.

At three o'clock we all watched the Queen on television. My father made us stand up while the national anthem was played. He did not have strong views on the Queen herself, but thought Mountbatten, whom he had met in the navy, 'a most frightful shit and probably a bugger-boy'.

At four o'clock we opened our presents round the tree.

I never knew what to give my father, apart from the new cartoons by Giles or Charles Adams, or the occasional book on naval history. When I was ten, I had given him a scarf I had knitted while bedridden with bronchitis. It was dark red, the colour I associated with my father. My father never wore the scarf and I never saw it again.

When my brother was eight, my father had given him a cricket bat, hoping he would be good at cricket. (He was furious with my mother for defending my brother in his choice not to box at prep school. My brother wasn't interested in cricket either.)

When we were children, Luke and I had performed plays at Christmas, written by me. One year it was a thriller called *Murder at Maudie's*. My brother, aged eight, had appeared as Maudie, a local Catholic widow, wearing a long skirt and an enormous hat decorated with paper flowers.

Another year we performed a play which I had based partly on the Addams family cartoons and partly on the character

Cruella de Vil from Dodie Smith's book *The One Hundred and One Dalmatians*. My Catholic upbringing had influenced the play. My brother was dressed as Lucifer, in a strange frock-coat of brown canvas from my grandmother's dressing-up box. I was Cruella de Vil, all in black. Our children, two dolls, I had named Graveyard and Coffin, perhaps in an unconscious echo of the fates of both my two brothers. In the first act Luke had started laughing nervously so I hit him. He cried and refused to continue. The adults thought at first that this was part of the play. We were devils, supposed to fight.

I do not remember my father ever attending my plays. He was too impatient, or jealous that his own theatrical ability had never been properly expressed or perhaps he was simply bored.

My mother's cousin Dermot, a retired major and a widower, lived only a few miles away and often came over for Christmas Day and Boxing Day. He had superficially much better manners than my father, except for one habit which my father found infuriating. He had lived in the Middle East and there had developed the habit of 'dropping in', without telephoning. My father deplored this.

'It's that bloody Dermot! Why the hell does he have to "drop in"? Why can't he telephone?' my father would shout.

He was also suspicious – perhaps rightly – when Dermot made a sudden appearance in my bedroom just after my eleventh birthday, when I was wearing nothing but vest and pants. With an unflagging interest in sex himself, my father seemed to have alert antennae which picked up other people's sexual interests, perhaps even before they themselves were aware of them. (When he had lived in Madrid, my father had guessed for some time that two expatriates were having an illicit affair and wasn't at all surprised when they eventually eloped together.)

At the age of fifteen I started going to local Christmas drinks parties with my parents. My father was popular in the neighbourhood, despite being banned by the local golf club for using bad language. Some were afraid of his abruptness – one perceptive young man pointed out that my father's bluntness arose from shyness; he would charge into a room, eyes down – but others, such as Dear Little Moppie, admired his outspokenness and found him original. (Dear Little Moppie had called him a 'breath of fresh air'.)

This Christmas one of my father's other favourites, Dear Little Hermia, was giving a cocktail party. (She lived in a Queen Anne house and was married to a stockbroker.) Just before we left, my father managed to bump into her so that she dropped the tray she was carrying and smashed a whole load of glasses. I was surprised that Hermia did not seem annoyed. Perhaps, unlike my father, she simply had very good manners.

After this humiliating incident my father sang his favourite song all the way home:

> I'm doing
> Spermia
> With Hermia.
> Spermia
> With Hermia's
> Great fun!

I did not know then that it was nearly my father's last Christmas.

As for Andrew and his family, I had gone over there for lunch on Boxing Day. His father, a Scot, was, like my own father, a colourful character. He described how he had been sacked as a young man by his newspaper and had found himself wandering destitute along the Embankment.

'Why were you fired?' I asked.

'Incompetence.'

Andrew's mother worked tirelessly to cook delicious meals and, besides her husband and three grown-up sons, she ministered to a pair of silky blond Labradors and several Shetland ponies. After lunch some of us played backgammon. I realized that, despite his previous outlandish behaviour – storming his father's club wearing women's clothes and giving up his successful job to live in a gay commune – Andrew was accepted at home in a way that Luke was not accepted by *my* father.

Harvey

Although I had split up with Peter, I was still working every day at the law centre.

'Awful old hole, really,' Mark, one of the solicitors, remarked as he was cleaning its windows. It was an old butcher's shop.

I was sitting at the switchboard.

'Were the law centres like this in Canada?' I asked.

'Certainly not. They were prepared to spend more money for one thing. Look at this entrance. It's really uninviting. It's dreadful to have to put your head through a hole to ask what you want.'

'Perhaps we receptionists are afraid of being bashed on the head,' I suggested.

'Oh, I don't think so,' Mark looked shocked. 'I don't think our clients are that bad.'

I laughed. I often teased Mark, who took himself very seriously. He had starry-blue eyes like Frank Sinatra. I thought he worked at the law centre partly because he felt it was more avant-garde than being an ordinary solicitor. Also, he had a firm belief that law centres would spring up all over London in a very short time (which in fact they did) and he would then have been one of the pioneers.

When he was in court, he became very excited and each time behaved as if he were involved in a murder case instead of a rent reduction of a few pounds. He called most of the clients sir and madam; his manner was more suited to a hairdressing establishment than to a law centre near Harrow Road.

That afternoon the door opened and a bowed woman with dank hair and droopy eyes came in. She had a strong Scottish accent.

'I've come to see Mr What's-his-name Gaites,' she said. 'Awful weather.'

'What's your name, madam?' asked Mark, in a most polite voice, and rushed for the switchboard, which I was supposed to be operating. He buzzed for Mike Gaites, the head solicitor. 'Mrs Carnegie here to see you.'

A curse came down the other end.

'Please could you wait in our hall. Here in front of the fire,' said Mark.

Mrs Carnegie sat down. She was dressed as if to imitate Guy Fawkes, her clothes slung on any old how. She looked very bulky, probably because all her clothes were old.

'I know I'm early,' she said. 'I shouldn't have come at all. Doctor's orders are to stay in bed. I've got bronchial pneumonia. My son's got it too. It's these new flats. The ones by the gas works. They're all damp. It's no good with six kids.'

'I'm going upstairs to Jane's room,' said Mark. 'Buzz me if you're in any trouble.'

He disappeared upstairs.

'Well, I must say this is a nuisance,' said Mrs Carnegie. 'I've a good mind not to go to court at all. It's the first time my son's been in any trouble. That's what comes of living in those flats. I tell him not to talk to those people. But you know what young people are.'

'Which people?' I asked.

'The black people in the flat at the back. I've nothing against black people, mind. But it's this woman. She's a teacher too, you wouldn't believe it. She clouted my son one. So I clouted her back. You're not going to stand by and see your young ones getting it in the neck, are you? She thought she'd be safe when she got the police, but I clouted her again in front of them. That's why I'm here.'

Just then Mike Gaites, who ran the law centre, and who had started it with another man, came in. His face was chalk-white as always. He was overworked. He spoke to Mrs Carnegie in a curt, bored tone.

'Well, Mrs Carnegie? Why didn't you come in yesterday? You won't get out of trouble if you don't turn up, you know. The police officer's arriving today to hear your statement. They're sick of waiting, I can tell you.'

'I'm not supposed to be out of bed at all,' she replied. 'You wouldn't come here if you had bronchial pneumonia as I have.'

'Mrs Carnegie, I've been here with flu, gastroenteritis, glandular fever and measles. If you hadn't lost your temper, you wouldn't be here at all. Every time you fail to put in an appearance the police will be less disposed in your favour. Now, where's Tom? It's no good without him.'

Mrs Carnegie sat back and crossed her legs. She folded her coat more tightly about her. 'Tom's gone up the Harrow Road after a job. I can't go supporting him any more with five others. It won't look so good in the witness box if he hasn't got a job. Specially with that long hair. What will they think?'

Mike Gaites narrowed his eyes. He had a commanding presence. 'Mrs Carnegie, this is no time to go looking for a job. Either you get him and you win the case, or you lose. I've got plenty of other clients on my hands.'

'All right, sir.' Mrs Carnegie looked slightly more acquiescent.

'Now, you wait here, and come and see me upstairs in a quarter of an hour.' He went upstairs and slammed his door.

Mrs Carnegie sat with her head thrown back against the steaming windows. An old man passed carrying a bag of vegetables. He tripped and nearly fell over.

'Awful old drunk,' remarked Mrs Carnegie. 'I've seen him in the Warwick Castle. Making a fool of himself. Bloody Irish.'

'Oh, I like him,' I said.

The Irishman was always being taken in for being drunk and disorderly. His name was Mr Power.

Mrs Carnegie became quiet and started reading a copy of *Woman's Own* that she had pulled out of her bag.

Without Peter's influence, I had almost lost sight of the original motives I'd had for working at the law centre. (One

our local town. Both men were called Tony. Tony Number One's dismembered body, several months after he disappeared, had been found in the grounds of my old school (the one where I had gone, aged seven, soon after Jonathan was drowned) by some Boy Scouts who were camping there in the summer holidays.

My father described, as we ate sauerkraut – my parents now had a Czechoslovakian cook who was a refugee – how a finger was held up in court as evidence. Tony Number Two, who had confessed to the murder of his friend (probably also his lover), explained in court how the ghost of Tony Number One had soon afterwards appeared to him saying, 'Tony, I've forgiven you.'

I was now sharing my house in Hackney with Ian and Carla. I had met them on that skiing holiday in Poland in February, a few days after Peter had proposed to me in The Intrepid Fox.

On our first night in Warsaw Carla and I had shared a bedroom in the hotel. She had been worried that Ian, who had just left Cambridge and was very handsome, liked another girl in our group. However, by the next evening Carla had 'got' Ian, simply by being persistent, and in the hostel in Zakopane, where we had all stayed for twelve days, she had managed to persuade him to let her share his bedroom. (As a result the equal distribution of the sexes was muddled up and I had to sleep on the floor with two other girls for ten days.)

Carla was not typical of most American girls of our age or, indeed, of our generation. Other girls mostly wore blue jeans, smoked dope and had no ambition, or, if they did, they didn't admit to it. Carla, every morning before setting off for her acting school, made up her face with false eyelashes, foundation and rouge. She wanted to be a film star. With her red lips, dark eyes and cascading brown hair, she looked overblown and sultry, the type that appealed particularly to older men. Her father had abandoned her and her mother when she was three, after losing a fortune in real estate. Now he was wandering around America with a religious sect.

Carla's first lover, or sugar-daddy, had been a middle-aged man from Chicago who had made a fortune out of pinball machines. Carla had met him at his own daughter's 'skinny-dipping' party. He had then taken Carla for drives along freeways outside Chicago and they had finally 'balled', as Carla called it, in a Holiday Inn. He made frequent expensive telephone calls to her now in England and had even sent her a gold watch for her twenty-first birthday.

Carla's attitude to sex seemed distorted and somewhat hysterical. She talked freely about 'clap clinics', 'prophylactics' and 'climaxes', but did not seem to see sex as a matter of enjoyment.

Ian and I were always teasing Carla about her American expressions. She pronounced 'body' as 'bahdy'. Whenever she said this word, 'bahdy', Ian and I would yell with laughter.

We invented stories to tell her as she was so gullible. One was about Rosie-Anne, the Filipino girl I had met in the hostel for women in Chicago, just before I had travelled round America with Martin on the Greyhound buses. (Rosie-Anne, a Catholic, kept a rosary by her bed and wore matching shoes and handbag. She had come to England and was now a nanny to a rich family near Regent's Park.)

Ian and I told Carla that Rosie-Anne was a stripper in her spare time. We said we had seen her perform at The King Cock Club in Soho.

'Not that sweet little Rosie-Anne!' said Carla, shocked.

Carla and Ian's relationship wasn't satisfactory for either of them. He was too fastidious. He was so handsome, with his thick lips, brown eyes and curly brown hair. He looked brawny, but this was misleading. He was narcissistic and had a leather sponge-bag full of different medicines – Bonjela for mouth ulcers, TCP, Carter's Little Liver Pills. He ate health food, was a vegetarian and enjoyed wearing soft cotton shirts. He had a gold ear-ring in one ear.

Ian was always trying to end his relationship with Carla, who was more promiscuous than he was. The last time they had 'balled' was when I was out buying vegetables in Chapel Market one Saturday. (Ian had told me about it later. Carla had flung herself on top of him, shrieking, 'I want to ball. Why not, balling's balling!')

Ian thought sex should be taken more seriously. This was perhaps why he and I hadn't 'balled', although Carla was always urging us to go ahead.

'Why don't you fellers ball? You might enjoy it.'

Or she would say privately to me, 'I'll lend you Ian for a night, if you like. He's nice to ball.'

But Ian and I remained just friends, although I was attracted to him and perhaps he was to me. One day he took photographs of us with his flash camera. Carla was nude, but I only took off my top half. When the photos were developed, Carla looked murky and scared, and I looked like a hamster.

About this time I had an article published in the *Guardian*. (A friend of Andrew worked on the economics pages and had asked me to write a review of a pamphlet about the Green Revolution in India.)

My mother was pleased I had been published in a newspaper, but my father did not seem that impressed. He was even slightly mocking. Although he sometimes gave me off-the-cuff literary advice – such as never to use a long word if a simple one would do – I realized that I could not look to him for any encouragement. As Rose had once pointed out when we were still teenagers, my father – indeed, both my parents – had 'dropped out' long ago.

I sat in the law centre, biting the top of my pen. I felt my life was dead. I did not know how to get anything else published. The cherry blossom was out in Ladbroke Grove, but it seemed false against the drizzling sky. My feet were wet, my hair was greasy and my face was white from too much London air. I had had boiled cabbage for lunch.

I arrived back in Hackney that evening and found the kitchen in darkness. Ian was upstairs. I yelled to him and he appeared at the bathroom door with a purple bath towel tied round his waist.

I had never seen him naked. He enjoyed showing off his torso, though. He was vain, in an agreeable way. He stood grinning in the bathroom doorway.

'Where's Carla?' I asked.

'I think she's trying to seduce Duke,' said Ian. 'I told her all young girls like homosexuals because they think they're safe, but she's convinced she's in love with him.'

Duke was a student at Carla's acting school. She had to kiss him in the play they were doing. He wasn't interested in her. He preferred a fair-haired student called Daniel.

'Did you hear her being sick in the bath last night?' said Ian. 'When we got back from the party? She was drunk before we even arrived at the dance. Too many of the Copelands' champagne cocktails.' He laughed. He had rather a rich laugh.

'Are you having a bath?' I said unnecessarily.

I looked right in. The windows were steamed up. There were no curtains. By the lavatory was a cutting of an American policeman beating up a student at the Chicago Convention. The student's head was bloody. I had put it up over a year ago, to remind myself of my own visit to Chicago.

'I was just about to.'

Ian had studied English at Cambridge, but had never participated in university life, preferring to sit alone in his room, reading and listening to Beethoven. He had not used his degree to get a job. Instead, he had sold ice-creams in Manchester and then worked on a pipeline, where his companions told stories about sheep-shagging. When he had come to London, Ian's father had found him a job with an advertising agency. He hated it, and was talking about becoming a bus conductor.

He told me this now.

'Well, yes, then at least you'd meet the common man,' I said.

'The common man' was a phrase Ian and I used often. It meant 'the average person'. I would say to Ian, 'What's the good of my being a writer if the common man doesn't read what I write?' or he would say, 'I want you to collect a pair of bathroom scales for me, from the Green Shield Stamp place, with my coupons. It'll be another opportunity for you to meet the common man.'

Ian had had more opportunity in his childhood to meet the common man than I had. His father owned a pub. But Ian's parents wanted him to make the most of his university degree. His mother especially was disappointed about his apparent lack of ambition.

'Would your father mind your being a bus conductor?' I asked. 'Or would he prefer you to become a butler in Beverly Hills?' (Ian had just answered an ad in *Time Out*: 'Butler wanted in Beverly Hills. Good-looking, not gay. Must like dogs.' He had not yet had a response.)

Ian replied that his father, who, like mine, had been in the navy, would admire his son's sense of adventure if he went to California. He would probably not even mind him immersing himself in the world of the proletariat, on a bus. His mother, however, would.

I had met his mother, Mrs Bartlow, a couple of times and liked her. Ian said the main reason she had married his father was that his father brushed his teeth after every meal. Carla blamed Ian's obsession with hygiene, his vegetarianism, even her own 'climaxes manqués', on Ian's mother.

'Well, send off a letter to London Transport,' I said.

Ian said he already had sent a letter off that morning from his office, while he was supposed to be writing a description of an American garbage disposal unit.

Both Ian and Carla were keen for me to get a new boyfriend. Ian had known Peter by sight at Cambridge, but their paths hadn't crossed. Peter had a high profile even then as a militant leftie.

'Why don't you ball Harvey?' Carla suggested later that evening, referring to an American student at her acting school. 'He's supposed to be having a party on Saturday. I'm sure he finds you attractive. Anyway, you must get Peter out of your system.'

A few nights later the four of us were in Harvey's bedsit, waiting for the other guests to arrive. To allay our boredom and delude ourselves that there was some kind of festivity going on we drank two whole bottles of Italian wine in fifteen minutes. The only effect of this was to give me a headache and make Harvey come out with more clichés than usual. I found out later that he had taken Ian aside and said in a terse voice, 'I'm going to get her tonight.'

Ian knew Harvey had meant me. He admitted that he had given Harvey a thumbs-up sign.

Meanwhile I was sitting on the sofa wearing white eye make-up and no bra. Harvey leaned forward, looking, with his beaky nose and tiny eyes, like an earnest hen.

'You look very attractive,' he said.

'Oh good,' I said. I had been considering whether or not to go to bed with him for a few days.

When I finally did, it was a surprise.

Never had I known sensations like this. This was why female cats screamed at night, for this mixture of pain and pleasure. I wanted to fuck all day. When he had gone, I lay and remembered what it was like. I had never been completely taken out of myself before.

Harvey was very virile in bed. Out of it he was tall, pale, skinny and undecided, with a few spots on his face. He lived mainly on a diet of fish and chips. In his bedsit he sat most of the day smoking dope. One of his favourite expressions was 'I'm bushed, man.'

Ian and Carla invited Harvey to move in with us. According to Ian he had agreed, saying, 'I want to be with people I love.' But he did not come.

'Perhaps he doesn't love us any longer,' said Ian.

Actually I had liked Harvey better before he became my lover. I remembered drinking with him one night in the Island Queen, after another student party. We had come home and played

Leadbelly records. My favourite Leadbelly song was 'Goodnight Irene'.

Harvey told me that when he was a little boy, he had fallen down a cliff and clung with one hand to a shrub for half an hour, before being rescued. 'I thought I would die.'

I described how, in a dream, I had seen my ex-boyfriend beheaded.

'With such a strong subconscious, you must become a writer,' said Harvey.

One day he told me, 'I am an artist.'

I suppose he imagines being drunk and stoned all day is what artists do, I thought.

After the weekend when he made love to me I felt lonely. The lady who worked in the local launderette in New North Road noticed it. She was kind, bending over me as if she wanted to chat, helping me with the machine. I told her I worked in Soho. (I had just applied for another publishing job.)

'Are you one of them strippers?' she asked.

Two other women were talking about some raffle tickets they had bought, and what they would do if they won the prize.

We can't think of anything to say to each other, I thought. I'm an outsider in this launderette.

Carla and I went down to Devon in my car. Ian and Harvey were to join us the next day.

The house was damp as it was only March. In the sitting-room there was a picture of ducks flying against the moon. We slept in a room overlooking the sea. Carla was wearing some all-in-one pyjamas, bright yellow.

'My first boyfriend, Mark, gave them to me,' she explained. 'He bought them in Alaska. They're called Dr Dentons.'

'These sheets are terribly damp, aren't they?' I said.

'The only thing to keep one warm are Dr Dentons and the "bahdy" of Ian Bartlow,' said Carla vulgarly.

She began chattering about contraceptives, but I was listening instead to the sound of the sea. It was either desolate, or peaceful, according to one's mood.

The next morning I took Carla down to the beach.

'I used to play here when I was a child,' I said. 'These rocks were my house.'

I stood underneath the sea-wall. The pink rock with water in its crack had been the bathroom.

Carla was wearing her new red wig. It looked incongruous on the beach.

'Let's go and walk on the cliffs.'

Up there the grass was covered with tiny pink flowers, like the flowers I had seen when I had taken LSD that time with my brother. We lay among the flowers, watching the sea below, and the red earth on the cliff face. Carla talked about her childhood.

'Ian reminds me of my father. They both want to be rich, but they won't work. I can't take Ian seriously... My stepsister's mother tried to turn her against her dad after he married my mom. When she was fourteen, my stepsister said, "I'm going to soak my father for every penny he's got."'

'How unpleasant,' I said. 'What a fucked-up American childhood.'

I was lying with my face up to the sky. A pale-yellow sun had come out.

'The only times I feel happy are in the country,' Carla said. 'Then I can feel like a kid again.'

That evening Carla and I fetched Ian and Harvey from the station. Then we walked across the beach to the local pub.

I told Harvey, 'I used to draw a woman on this beach. Her name was Miss Adderness. She had a forked tongue.'

I took off my shoes to cross a stream.

'How cold the sand is!' I exclaimed.

'Put on your shoes.' Harvey stood waiting for me. He made me feel like a little girl. 'Put on your shoes.'

I put them on. Really he's quite kind, I thought. But I have no idea what he's thinking. Perhaps he's only thinking of beer.

'Why don't you ball Harvey tonight?' Ian whispered to me later in the pub. 'You're a good couple. Harvey can mount you like a man.' He grinned. I thought that he wanted me to have a good lover because he was fond of me.

'Well, I don't know,' I said.

I put a coin into the juke-box. The record I chose was 'Union Man'. The words were: 'I'm a Union Man. I get what I can. I say what I think – that the company stinks. I'm a Union Man.'

'You only put that on because it reminds you of that bigoted communist,' Ian accused me. 'You're still obsessed with him.'

'No I'm not.'

Carla was talking to a fisherman at the bar. I thought it was unlike her. She was rather materialistic and preferred men with money. On the way back along the beach Ian and Harvey were very cheerful as they had drunk so much beer.

Ian ran and plunged into the dark sea, getting his jeans wet under the moon, letting out war cries.

'He's so unhappy. That advertising job's killing him,' said Carla.

When Ian came out of the sea, she was very affectionate, calling him 'my poor baby' and kissing the nape of his neck. In the kitchen she wrung out his jeans and hung them up to dry.

A few days later I was sitting in the kitchen in Hackney. It was badly lit. There was a smell of dead rat. On the wall was a communist poster, of the prime minister's head being squeezed by a giant communist fist. Peter had put it there. Perhaps it was time to take it down. I looked in the cupboard to see if there was any food, but there was only some revolting dried stuff which Ian ate instead of meat.

It was time to move on. I had been turned down for a job on the *Time Out* agit-prop page – I had got on a shortlist of four, probably because I had collected underground newspapers – but when asked what my political convictions were, I had replied, 'I think we're all very confused.'

I was supposed to go on holiday in April with Harvey to Morocco, but whenever I tried to discuss plans Harvey said he was 'bushed'. I explained that I would have to know soon, otherwise I wanted to travel to Italy with Carla.

Now Carla had left for Italy, by train, with an American girl from her drama school. Ian had finally been interviewed for the butler's job advertised in *Time Out*. He had gone to meet his future employer's representative in Charing Cross Station. (The only other applicant, also waiting at the departures board, had been an Italian waiter with a broken jaw.) Ian was offered the job at once. He was due to start in Los Angeles in three weeks. I wasn't sure if I would be back in England before he left.

Two days before Harvey and I were to leave for Morocco I went round to his bedsit and rang the bell. There was no answer so I knocked on the door of the flat upstairs, which was occupied by two other students from his drama school.

'Oh, he went to Barcelona yesterday with Lana, that blonde girl in the class below us,' a girl with a ponytail told me.

Luckily Carla telephoned that night from Florence and invited me to join her out there. We agreed to travel on together from Italy to Greece.

Philippe

After an uncomfortable night sitting up in a train through Italy, Carla and I arrived in Brindisi. We walked through the town to the harbour, being whistled at by young Italian men.

Scarcely had we sat down with our legs dangling over the quayside, when several of them swooped upon us and tried to engage our interest. One well-dressed boy said he had lived in Trafalgar Square. He offered to drive Carla to look at some beaches. She said yes, so he left to get his car.

Meanwhile another Italian boy, who was only twenty, tried to establish rapport with me by mentioning various Beatles songs. I said I did not like the Beatles. He then produced the words of a song he had written himself, scribbled on a piece of paper. Translated, the words were as follows: 'Oh, world of hippie, oh, world of hippie, oh, wonderful world of hippie!'

'Very good!' I said. 'Do they have many hippies in Italy?'

'No.'

He pressed a photo into my hand of himself looking like a demented monkey.

At twilight Carla had a brief romantic interlude with a black man in a leather hat. She had been watching him for some time. 'Isn't he cute?' she kept saying.

'Yes, quite,' I replied.

'I've got something in my eye,' said Carla. 'Do you think I could ask him for a mirror?'

After I had peered into Carla's right eye, discovered a piece of red wool and failed to extract it, I decided that she could indeed ask the man for a mirror. Within two minutes she was in his arms and his tongue was in her eye.

Carla came back smiling blissfully. 'It's gone,' she said. 'He kissed it away. Did you see?'

'Yes,' I replied shortly. 'I was amazed to see you in such a position.'

The black man grinned at us both.

Five days later, after a night on a boat to Patras feeling seasick, three nights in a youth hostel in Corfu and one night in a ghastly hotel in Athens called Mary's Hostel run by a man who looked like the devil, Carla and I arrived in Crete. (We had meant to sail to Iráklion, but took the wrong ferry and ended up in the port of Khaniá.)

After Carla had 'washed up', as she called it, we went for a stroll. We were soon picked up by two Greek boys, one with long black hair and a serious expression, the other with cropped curly hair and a sweet elfin face. They led us into an empty hotel and on to a balcony, where they ordered Nescafé and Cokes. The one with long hair became my beau. He was rebellious and said he hated Americans. He was about to go into the Greek army. He did not want to, but it was difficult to get a passport to leave Greece because he was an 'enemy of the government'.

'The tourists come here and say, "Greece is marvellous." In America, I've heard, you can't walk the streets at night. But the tourists have no idea what's really going on.'

Just then an American with very short hair came and sat next to us. The long-haired Greek, whose name was Nikos, made a face of contempt. 'The American navy!' he said.

Carla leaned across to the American and began to talk animatedly about Wisconsin. The American was affable, sincere and superficial.

'But why are you here at all? Why is your navy in our waters?' asked my Greek aggressively.

'I guess to defend Greece,' said the American, still very affably.

'From what?' the Greek persisted.

'I guess they must think there's something worth defending,' he replied blandly.

'Let's go for a walk,' the other Greek suggested to us.

Carla immediately invited the American sailor to come with us. I kicked her for this *faux pas*.

On the way out of the hotel we met some more American sailors, all with short hair and baggy trousers. 'Hi,' they said.

The Greek who looked like an elf then left us.

'He's leaving the country to see his girlfriend in Denmark,' said Nikos darkly. He added in an undertone to me, 'He is not coming back. He can get a passport because he is not an "enemy of the government". I am.'

'Goodness!' I said. It was difficult to imagine what it was like to be confined to one country. We walked across the harbour, where there was an enormous sign of the Colonels – the silhouettes of armed men with rifles standing among flames.

'When they took over, they put another sign like that in front of the harbour,' said the Greek. 'The people of this town made them take it down.'

He and I sat in a café beside the water and drank ouzo. The waiter brought some delicious titbits. If you drank ouzo without food, it burned your insides. I tucked in to bits of octopus, olives, cheeses, snippets of lamb, tomatoes and peppers. The Greek fed himself from time to time.

'I have slept with forty women,' he announced. 'I do not like the girls of my own country. The girls at my university sell themselves to older men for five hundred drachmas. I have seen this many times.'

He told me that he had had an English girlfriend called Jane Fleck. She lived in Surbiton. 'We spent the whole of last summer together in Crete,' he said. 'We got to know each other very well.'

I wondered whether he wanted me to be another Jane Fleck. He pressed more ouzo on me. Then Carla and the American sailor came and joined us.

As soon as it was dark, a drunk Englishman called Geoffrey lurched up looking extraordinary. He sat down next to me, giggling nervously. Occasionally he lunged towards me, but always withdrew at the last moment. He tried to guess my profession. 'I think you're a *citoyen du monde.*'

He, like so many others, was anti-American. 'I lived in New

York till I was ten,' he said. 'The Americans are unimaginative, superficial and bad at relationships.'

This annoyed me, but I could say nothing in the face of such blind prejudice. 'What do you do in England?' I asked.

'I have my own radio programme,' he replied. 'I'm also a freelance journalist. I just sold an interview with William Burroughs to a newspaper for thirty pounds.'

The Greek did not particularly like Geoffrey flirting with me. Also, Geoffrey kept leaning over and helping himself to octopus with enormous fingers. Then he began playing chess with another Greek man who had joined us.

'They are like two schoolboys,' observed my Greek scathingly. 'You want to meet me here tomorrow morning at ten o'clock?'

'I think eleven would be better,' I said. 'I'd like to go to bed now,' I added.

Geoffrey immediately leaped up. 'I shall escort you to your hotel,' he said drunkenly. I followed him down the back streets.

'Have you any shampoo?' I asked him.

When we reached the hotel (his was the same one as ours), he hurried into his bedroom and presented me with two bottles.

'Dop and Vosene. Use them both, one after the other,' he said. He gazed after me uncertainly.

'What a creep!' said Carla next morning.

I went alone into the harbour to have breakfast. Geoffrey was already there, drinking retsina.

'Do you drink all day?' I asked.

'Yes,' he replied.

'Ah, that's why you walk so crooked,' I said.

'Yes, most of the time I feel as if I'm on a ship,' he admitted.

I ordered some fried eggs. Carla came in looking sulky. Geoffrey pulled up a chair. We began to quarrel in front of him about whether to leave Khaniá that day and go to Iráklion.

I said I did not like Khaniá. After all, we had only gone there by mistake. However, when I asked Carla if she wanted to stay, she refused to say yes or no. Therefore we spent the rest of the morning walking up and down the streets of Khaniá with

Geoffrey following us, while Carla found out various ways of preventing us from leaving without actually saying directly that she wanted to stay. We went to the bus station and she said the bus was too expensive. We then decided to hitch-hike. Carla triumphantly found a man in a car who told us this was far too difficult. I went furiously back to the hotel to wash my clothes. Carla went to the beach with Geoffrey.

Next morning we decided after all to take the bus to Iráklion. Carla, who had slept with Geoffrey the night before, was too embarrassed to say goodbye to him. I knocked on his door. He leaped out of bed without any clothes on, looking confused.

'We're going,' I said.

Then Carla went in. She came out looking shamefaced. She was disappointed that he did not ask for her address.

'Maybe he thinks you're only a one-night stand,' I said. 'Why didn't you leave a card?' I said, to tease her.

'Shut up,' said Carla.

In Iráklion we found a small hotel with a photograph of John F. Kennedy behind the desk.

The next morning Carla was bad-tempered. She had not many more days of her holiday left. To make matters worse, I had left my briefcase on the bus. I would have to go back to the bus station to look for it. I said goodbye to Carla, who was talking to two girls from Indiana.

Luckily my briefcase was in the bus station. While I was there, I had a conversation with an Australian girl who told me about a village on the south coast where people lived in caves.

'Dirty hippies!' said the girl. 'Burned-out Americans! If you want to go to the caves, you can see it all.'

This encounter with Australian prejudice made me decide to go to the village. It sounded a free sort of place.

My brother had frequently reminded me of how, when we had gone round the Greek islands on a yacht with our parents when I was thirteen and he was nine, as we anchored off the beach at Marathon, our father had stood on deck and quoted Byron, in an authoritative voice:

> 'The mountains look on Marathon –
> And Marathon looks on the sea.'

I associated the Greek islands with the unearthly and in-toxicating smell of pine trees.

My father would not have approved of the village I was going to as he disliked the idea of hippies. Both he and I had read James Michener's novel *The Drifters*, about a group of young people of different nationalities who had become friends in Torremolinos. My father had had strong reactions to all these fictional characters. His favourite was a Jewish boy called Yigal, who was already a military hero in Israel, and the one he disapproved of outright was seventeen-year-old Monica, a beautiful and promiscuous upper-class English girl, who, by the end of the book, had become a heroin addict and met a sordid death in Morocco.

I was puzzled by my father's hatred of this teenage girl. Perhaps she embodied aspects of his own life that he did not want to think deeply about – sexual promiscuity, which he nominally disapproved of, certainly in women, and his un-satisfactory relationship with his own son, who, like Monica, took drugs.

The Cretan bus started its slow journey through lovely places. We passed orange trees, grey-green mountains covered with cypresses, fields of poppies (a true red, not like the poppies in Italy which, in comparison, seemed anaemic, perhaps from car fumes) and olive trees with twisted trunks and silver leaves.

The valley of this village was the loveliest of all; I felt I had arrived in heaven. The wild flowers were as high as the waist, the sky was blue, the village itself was in a small cove from which, at the sea's horizon, you could see the outlines of black mountains, while to the east were higher mountains, covered with snow. A tiny group of oblong white houses was in the square.

At first it was difficult to see any Greeks at all. The people sitting around the square were Americans and other bohemians

130

or students; they nearly all wore jeans and had long hair. They looked as if they felt at home in the place.

My impressions that night were confused. I noticed that it seemed very wild. There was a wind on the beach; a few people sat on the sand close to the sea, the girls wearing long gypsyish skirts. A brown and black puppy rushed up and down the shore barking and biting at the girls' skirts.

I went to sleep in a cave to the sound of the sea.

The next day I followed a mountain path to a cove called Red Beach. Here there were nudists and tar. I did not take my clothes off as I had just arrived. I noticed one nudist, a caveman with long yellow hair, staring lustfully at my bare legs.

Later I saw the yellow-haired caveman again. I was in the Mermaid Café with two boys I had just met – Craig, a sophisticated American drop-out, living in Paris, and Michael, a blond Canadian whom Craig called his cave-buddy. Craig was wearing a freshly ironed white shirt, drank a great deal of ouzo and had startlingly blue eyes ringed with black. I liked Michael at once and was in awe of him. I also thought him attractive, and in some way grown-up, although he was so dangerously thin. He had probably been starving himself, trying to stretch out his traveller's cheques as long as possible.

We all had bean soup, which was on the menu every night.

'Do you know, the Mermaid Café is in a song by Joni Mitchell?' I said. 'Apparently it's about this café in Mátala. She sings about the tar upon her feet and she's sorry she left her honky-tonk piano back in the USA.'

'Don't be absurd,' Craig replied. 'She was singing about a café in Spain. She says she's going to dress up for a night in the Mermaid Café. I remember the words. Who on earth would dress up to come here?' (In fact I was right.)

Everyone laughed. Then the wild man, with long yellow hair, whom I had seen on the nudist beach came in, with a youthful follower. They sat down and began to play chess. The blond man was very energetic. I wondered what nationality he was. Then I heard him say something in French. For some reason I was glad.

131

Craig was watching the game of chess.

'Is he good?' I asked.

'He's a bit unorthodox,' Craig replied.

'Why don't you play him sometime?' I said.

'I might.'

The Frenchman nodded abruptly at me as I left with Craig and Michael.

The next day I was seduced on the Red Beach.

I went down alone, early in the morning. I walked along the rocks a little way, took off my clothes and began to sunbathe. I was reading a very funny book, *The Dice Man*. The main character was a New York psychiatrist who decided to liven up his life by throwing a die to determine his actions. I had got to the part where he had arranged for some of his patients, the occupants of a mental home, to go to a performance of the musical *Hair*, and escape by pretending to be members of the cast.

I laughed out loud. There was a cough behind me. I screamed with fright. The Frenchman from the Mermaid Café was standing behind me and grinning. He was naked.

'My God, you frightened me,' I said. 'I'm reading a very funny book.' I held it up.

'Not so fast!' replied my companion in French. 'I don't speak English . . . Would you like to come for a walk with me over those rocks? There is a little cove there no one knows about. My name is Philippe.'

He was a beautiful colour, that kind of ripe golden brown that only blond people have.

I rose and followed him over the rocks. He walked as if he had been climbing rocks all his life. He seemed very free. When it was steep, he turned and helped me up.

At last we rounded a corner and came to a sandy plateau above the sea. It was deserted.

'Come and lie down.'

He began to stroke me.

'I'm completely detached,' I warned him.

'I know.'

Soon, however, I was not so detached. 'Please be careful, I don't want to have a baby,' I said.

Philippe was rough. He kept asking me whether he hurt me.

'No, it's all right,' I said. It was very nice making love in the sun, on this wild coast.

'I've never made love outside before,' I told Philippe. 'In England it's usually very cold.'

Philippe seemed surprised at this. He put his arms round me as though he were an ape and smoothed down the hair on my arms. 'There, now you can go to Hollywood.'

All at once a cry came from the mountain above us. A figure stood up there, hundreds of feet up, at the top of the red rocks.

'Who's that?' I said.

'Oh, it's only a shepherd,' replied Philippe. 'We needn't worry. He also likes women.'

Philippe then began to talk about intellectual matters. He asked me if I had seen Godard's films, and whether I had read Dostoevsky. I told him I had read *The Idiot* on an aeroplane when I was fifteen.

'*The Idiot* is a brilliant book,' he said. 'Very profound.'

'Why is it profound?'

'It is profound because it makes you think and reflect,' said Philippe, in French.

'Well, what have you been doing?' said Craig a few hours later outside the grocery store. 'I came down to the Red Beach, but I didn't see you.'

'No, I was further along the coast,' I said. I picked up the book he was reading. It was *The Colossus of Maroussi* by Henry Miller.

'I read a bit of this once,' I said. 'I couldn't finish it. I thought his idea of Greece was over-romantic.'

I was relieved to be able to sit discussing books as if I were with Craig in some Paris café. It seemed eminently civilized, compared with the nudist beach.

'Let's go and watch the sunset,' said Craig.

Watching the sunset was a daily ritual here. People sat cross-legged on the beach, staring out to sea. Sometimes a man who lived in one of the beach rooms played the drums. As we sat there, the rocks at the side of the beach became very white. The sky was violet and orange. The sun disappeared slowly behind the black mountains.

'There's something very sad about sunset,' said Craig, as the sky grew dark. 'I think it's the finality.'

I made love again with Philippe on the beach the next day. Philippe asked me what my father did.

'He was a sailor,' I said. 'He now has a small farm.'

'My father is a *fonctionnaire* on the railways,' said Philippe.

'What's a *fonctionnaire*?' I asked.

'He's in administration,' said Philippe. He sounded indignant that I might have thought that his father was a mere ticket collector. 'We eat very well at home,' he said. 'My father likes wine with his meals.' He told me that he lived in Alsace-Lorraine.

'That's close to the borders of Germany,' I said.

'Yes, but we hate the Germans,' said Philippe. 'During the war the Nazis put the people of Alsace-Lorraine who refused to fight for them into concentration camps. There were two near where we live.'

'One of my cousins married a man from Alsace-Lorraine,' I said. 'Whenever he does anything my family don't approve of, they say, "Oh well, he's half German anyway."'

Philippe put his arms round me. He wanted to make love all the time. We were sitting on a rock nearer the beach. I did not know whether people on the beach could see us. I hoped not.

'I don't like making love if people can see us,' I told Philippe. 'I'm modest.'

'Too modest for me, then,' replied Philippe. 'I don't like modest women.'

We lay down behind a piece of rock that hid us from the beach. It was very beautiful where we were. If we looked along the coast, we could see miles and miles of red rocks. At the horizon of the sea was another island covered with black mountains. The

134

mountains to the right of us were topped with snow.

'After this I want to go to the Arab countries,' said Philippe.
'It's dangerous for a woman to go there,' he said tauntingly.

'Have you got any money?' I asked.

'No,' said Philippe. 'I left France in February with ten francs.
I haven't got one drachma.'

'How do you live?' I said.

Philippe shrugged. 'I don't eat much. When the police come
and ask people to show what money they've got, I go and hide
up on the hills. I've asked my brother to send me a hundred
francs. That's not much, though.'

'I think I'd like to swim,' I said. 'Is it all right to swim off this
rock?'

Philippe showed me where to swim. Afterwards we lay
together in the sun.

'Why do you bring that green bag on to the rock with you?'
said Philippe. 'What's in it?'

'My passport and my diary,' I said. 'I don't want to lose them.'

'All girls have diaries,' said Philippe.

A fat nude figure was walking towards us on the rocks. It
was a girl who had hitch-hiked from Italy, whose cave I had
been in two nights before.

'I know that girl,' I said. 'She's American.'

'The Americans are fools,' said Philippe. 'I've seen that girl
too. She's the biggest fool of all. And isn't she fat?'

Certainly, when the girl turned round, she had enormous
dimples in her behind.

'She's going back,' I said. Indeed, the girl had turned and
was walking back to the beach. She was picking her way over
the rocks rather self-consciously.

We decided to go back to the beach as well. On the way we
saw another figure sitting in the rocks. It had long hair.

'Who is it?' said Philippe. 'Is it my friend Ben?'

As we got nearer, we saw it was a girl. When we came up to
her, she turned and laughed at us in a hoarse sexy voice. Philippe
was intrigued. She had long black hair and looked more Mexican

135

than American. Her hair was hiding most of her body, but it was obvious she was slim.

'Ask her if she's going to play her flute,' said Philippe, who could speak no American or English.

The girl replied that she would not play it now, but would play it at sunset for Philippe on the mountains.

'Ask her whereabouts,' said Philippe.

I, however, had got fed up relaying messages. I went on to the beach. Philippe returned soon. He was behaving in a nervous way. He spread out his jeans and signalled to me to sit on them. He was being very nice to me. Then the sexy girl appeared again. Instead of trying to talk directly to Philippe in her bad French, she said something to me. She told me how she had just been bothered by two little Greek boys wearing clothes. 'I guess they didn't mean any harm.'

She laughed again in her hoarse way and shook her hair at Philippe. She certainly had a good body. Philippe obviously wanted to try to lay the girl. A lot of clichés about sex-mad Frenchmen rose in my mind. I also was furious with the girl for pretending to talk to me when really she was interested in Philippe. I hated female slyness.

The girl walked off round the rocks on her own carrying her flute.

Philippe started fussing over me again. He spread out his towel for me as well as his jeans. Then he asked me if I liked Beethoven. I laughed derisively.

After a few moments Philippe disappeared round the rocks after the girl. I hoped no one on the beach saw as it was humiliating. I went and talked to an Australian girl and her boyfriend. The boy told me that he had been in Goa, in the south of India, a hippie paradise. The Australian girl, who was a nurse, got up and plunged into the sea. She was wearing an ankle-length blanket tied round her shoulders.

'What an extraordinary thing to swim in,' I said to the boy.

'It's called a swamoon,' he told me. 'It's Australian. They're very comfortable.'

'What a good swimmer your girlfriend is,' I remarked. (The Australian nurse was doing a powerful crawl.)

'Yes, they teach them young in Australia,' said the boy.

I went back and put on my clothes. I could not decide whether it was worse to stay on the beach waiting for Philippe pretending nothing had happened or to go back to the village on my own like a rejected female. The more I thought about these two possibilities, the more annoyed I became. If Philippe thought I was the sort of girl to sit on the beach while he screwed some insincere American with long hair, he was wrong. I hastily put his jeans and jersey and coffee-coloured bathing pants into my polythene bag, and climbed up the mountain. I walked quickly to the far side of the village and put the clothes behind a tree.

Then I saw Craig, drinking ouzo in a café.

'I've just hidden someone's clothes,' I told him breathlessly. 'I'm afraid he'll take awful revenge. He insulted me.'

'How?' said Craig.

'It's too embarrassing to say,' I replied. 'But I assure you he insulted me. Anyway, if he beats me up, I hope you'll defend me.'

'I shall say I know nothing about it,' said Craig. 'I'm peace-loving. Would you like some ouzo?'

I took a few sips. But I was too nervous to appreciate it. I did not know how angry Philippe would be.

After a long time Philippe appeared. He was wearing someone else's jeans. He was almost in tears. 'Where are my clothes?' he said brokenly. 'Did you take them? Do you know where they are?'

I had not anticipated this result. I put on a very brisk manner. 'Yes, yes, I know where they are. Come with me.'

He shook his head mournfully. 'Surely it wasn't you who took them? Who could have taken them? Did you see?'

'I took them,' I said, in the same brisk tone.

But for some reason, Philippe still didn't believe me.

He followed me back to the village. He was completely shaken. He kept hugging me. The fact that he was so upset made me feel suddenly maternal.

137

'Come and meet my English friend Ben,' he said.

Ben's room was Philippe's refuge. He did all his cooking there on Ben's gas cooker, using Ben's food. In fact, I discovered, this was how Philippe kept himself alive.

Ben came originally from Manchester. He was older than most of the other people in Mátala. He had been there all winter, sketching and going for short walks. He was an intellectual, he said. In London he had worked at arts centres and fringe theatres, and for a short time on an anarchist magazine. He sometimes did interior decorating. He was pleased to meet me, partly because I was English, but also because he made it clear that he thought I was pretty. He took hold of me by the shoulders. He had a long black beard like a goat, small eyes and glasses. In his room he held court. Visitors came in all the time to borrow food and use the gas cooker. They also came in to ask advice. The room emanated a spiritual calm which was part of Ben's character. Philippe called him Le Baron.

'The Baron thinks he will have vegetable soup tonight,' said Ben. 'Perhaps Monsieur Philippe will make the soup.'

Philippe enjoyed his role as cook. He was very energetic, and proud of his cooking. Now, he brightened up and began to cut up tomatoes.

'Shall I do some?' I said.

'Yes, yes. Women must work.' He handed me a knife. (He was trying to be commanding, to make up for his weakness earlier on.)

'No, no, not like that. You must cut them smaller.'

Two Swiss boys came in, bringing some white bread and butter. I recognized them from the Mermaid Café. One of them was only sixteen. He admired Philippe.

'Shall we go and steal some more tomatoes tonight?' Philippe suggested. 'I won't be able to tomorrow because you're leaving and I won't have a car.'

The small Swiss boy nodded.

'We took all this bag last night,' said Philippe. He showed me. 'It was easy. From some fields quite near by.'

Ben was lying back on his bed. Every now and then he would suggest that someone go and buy some brown bread. I suspected he was lazy. The room was filthy. The only light was a small gas lamp above Ben's bed. The table was covered with old tins, bags of coffee and sugar. There was sand all over the floor.

'This soup will be delicious,' Philippe told everyone. 'Go and buy everyone some yoghurt,' he said to the other Swiss boy, not his admirer, whom he began to tease by accusing him of being Jewish. It was a game. You weren't supposed to be prejudiced, therefore you couldn't object to being called Jewish.

Ben talked to me about Crete.

'When I get tired of being stoned, I just take a trip round the island,' he said. 'There are some tiny villages where no one goes. Every village has a miller. A few months ago I went and did some sketching further down the coast.'

He showed me his sketchbook. It contained some splashy watercolours of sunsets. One of them was a branch of a tree.

'I like this one,' I said.

'That's the only one I didn't do myself,' said Ben.

'All right, the soup's ready,' said Philippe.

There weren't enough plates or spoons to go round. Also, they were filthy, but luckily this wasn't too noticeable in the dim light. Philippe used glasses and saucepans. I drank my soup and Philippe sat on the bed beside me. When we had finished the soup, Philippe leaped upon me and started rubbing my back and breasts in a playful manner. Ben looked at us from the other bed. I thought he also wanted to sleep with me. This made me feel irritated.

Philippe made the tea and passed it round. He asked the two young Swiss boys to come to the bistro with him.

'What bistro?' I said. I discovered that Philippe meant the Mermaid Café.

'I'll be back later,' Philippe told me. I was piqued that he didn't ask me to go with them.

'You can stay the night here,' said Ben to me.

I persuaded myself that really he only meant 'stay the night'.

139

'I have to go and see what my friend Craig is doing,' I said. 'I might come back later.'

'Yes, do,' said Ben.

Craig and Michael were sitting in the square with a Spaniard.

'I came to see what you're doing,' I said to Craig.

'You didn't come to see that,' said Michael accusingly.

'What do you mean?' I said.

'Who's this?' asked the Spaniard.

'Craig's girlfriend,' said Michael. 'What have you been doing?' he continued. 'Hiding people's clothes? Grow up.' He was laughing. 'You must respect people more,' he said.

Craig was completely drunk. I felt a surge of affection for him.

'I'll help you back to your cave,' I said.

Michael and I made a slow procession back to their cave, Craig tripping up all the time.

'Where's your sleeping-bag?' I said maternally when we got there. Craig didn't have one. He got into Michael's sleeping-bag and collapsed.

'You can stay the night here if you like,' said Michael. 'There's plenty of room.'

I knew he was not trying to seduce me. I had a moment of calm. 'Well, I've been offered a bed by an Englishman,' I said. 'But I'll come back later if that doesn't work out.'

Michael made me feel peaceful. He was the only person in the village I had met so far who seemed to have worked out some sort of philosophy for himself. He was critical – he kept his own standards – but also generous and tolerant. I thought the most sensible thing to do would be to get my sleeping-bag and sleep alone under the trees. Philippe had disappeared.

I was too overexcited to remain on my own. It was as though I were being carried on a stream of events that I couldn't control, or didn't want to.

'Good, you've come back,' said Ben.

He took hold of my shoulders. The door was pushed open and a girl came in. Ben introduced her as Lola and said she was a Hare Krishna fanatic.

She looked at me antagonistically. 'Are you staying here?'

'Yes, she is,' said Ben firmly.

Lola sat on the bed. 'It was nice the way the room was arranged before, when I was here, wasn't it? The two beds close together. I've been here all winter,' she told me.

'Lola, I must go to bed now,' said Ben.

Lola left the room scowling. Ben firmly locked the door. Outside rose the loud strains of the Hare Krishna chant.

'She's trying to put us off,' I said.

'Take no notice,' said Ben.

However, the Hare Krishna chant continued for at least half an hour. Soon it was accompanied by drums. Lola had obviously asked a drummer to join her, to create even more disturbance. I laughed about this.

I did not enjoy making love with Ben at all. He did, though. In the early hours of the morning he told me about a girlfriend he had had from Liverpool. 'I had a relationship with her for two years,' he said. 'Once she got a contraceptive stuck inside her. I helped to get it out.'

I noticed that I preferred men who treated me roughly rather than ones who understandingly helped to get a contraceptive out when it was stuck. Also, I hated the word 'relationship'. I resolved never to sleep with anyone like that again. I left Ben's room as early in the morning as I could, declining his offer of tea. I lay on the beach on my own. After a couple of hours Craig turned up near the café. I joined him for breakfast.

'Will you come to Phaistós with me this morning?' he asked. 'We might even travel on further.'

'Yes, I think so,' I replied. 'I'd like to see the ruins and I'd like to travel round the island.'

Then I saw Philippe. I felt very ashamed.

'Are you leaving this morning?' he said gruffly, looking at my sleeping-bag.

'Yes,' I said.

Philippe disappeared. He came back again, saying, 'I've asked the Swiss boys to take you in their car. They're driving to Iráklion.

141

The younger boy is very nice. He was marvellous when we were stealing tomatoes.'

Then Philippe saw Craig and realized that he was going with me. 'He can pay you something. He's rich. He's American,' he said to the Swiss boys.

Philippe walked off.

Before the car started, I saw Ben, sitting on a bench. 'Please tell Philippe I said goodbye,' I said.

The Swiss boys let us out near Phaistós. Craig told me his father was an investment banker in the US.

'I dropped out of college,' said Craig. 'I took a few jobs, but I was always fired. Then I inherited some money.'

'What else do you do?' I asked.

'Play music to cinema queues in Paris,' he said. 'You can make forty dollars a day. My girlfriend and I choose our queues carefully. We go to the cinemas near the Étoile. And we play good-quality music. It's very irritating when guys who think they're musicians come and steal our queues when they're only in Paris for a day. They're usually Americans. My girlfriend's hot-tempered. She has gypsy blood.'

At Phaistós we were so hot and hungry that instead of seeing the ruins all we wanted was something to eat and drink. Luckily there was a restaurant. It was full of older tourists, including several Germans with expensive cameras.

'There's a shower in the ladies,' I told Craig delightedly. 'I'll use it before we leave.'

'Have you got a towel?'

'No. It doesn't matter. I didn't have in Mátala either.'

It was the first formal meal I'd had for some time. Craig was like a self-indulgent old man in a club. Unlike most of the young travellers, he ordered wine and meat without even looking at the price. Unlike the rest of us, he didn't have a sleeping-bag and his suitcase was new, made of cream-coloured leather.

'I don't like hitch-hiking,' he confessed.

After lunch we were both drunk. We wandered round the ruins, not taking in anything, following some Canadian tourists and a guide. The women looked like enormous grotesque dolls, with their peroxided hair and their pastel clothes.

'In Crete we have time for everything,' Craig and I overheard the guide say. 'There is always time.'

'Well, *we* only have three days,' replied one of the dolls.

The Cretans were kind about giving lifts. Despite Craig's dislike of hitch-hiking, we got a lift that evening back to Mátala in a green van with three wheels. The man who owned this one was called Manolo. He had short legs and a moustache. He obviously thought picking up hitch-hikers was a great joke. When he opened the back of his van to let me and Craig in, there were already two other hitch-hikers inside. By the time we arrived in Mátala there were ten of us.

'I'm going to put my things under the trees,' I said to Craig.

I walked over to the beach. I sat under the trees, on the sand. Near by was a man with bloodshot eyes.

Then I saw Philippe. He was outside Ben's room. It was easy to notice him from a distance because his hair was so blond that it looked as if he had no hair at all. At first he did not see me. I knew he had noticed me when he began swinging himself backwards and forwards around some posts. He was an awful show-off.

After about half an hour, after Craig had gone back to his cave, Philippe came over.

'I wasn't sure it was you,' he said.

It was nearly sunset.

'Come up on to those rocks with me and watch the sunset,' said Philippe. He led me up the cliff, around a corner to some rocks that looked right on to the sea, where no one could see us from the beach. Here the rocks were a sort of greyish-biscuit colour. The sun was already almost down. Philippe began to take off my clothes.

'Why did you come back?' he said.

'I don't know,' I said.

'Well, Ben will be pleased,' said Philippe. Soon we climbed down the rocks again.

'After you left today, I made love with a German,' said Philippe. 'She bit me. It was most unpleasant.'

'I hitch-hiked once with a German,' I said. 'A racist.'

We walked across the beach to Ben's room. Ben looked confused to see me. I was also embarrassed.

'Since this afternoon, there's an Italian living in Ben's room,' said Philippe. 'He smells. Also he farts. But after he's left, you could have the other bed.'

I did not say anything. I did not want to share Ben's room.

The next day Philippe and I made love on our rock near the Red Beach. It was peaceful. A fishing boat was going past. Afterwards Philippe said, 'Et ton américain?' His eyes appeared to fill with tears.

I said, 'Je n'ai pas d'américain. Qui?' I realized he meant Craig.

Philippe said, 'Don't play the innocent.'

Then he folded *Le Monde* into a paper hat and put it on his head, so that he looked like Napoleon.

In the evening the police came to the village. They walked round smiling at everybody and asked a few people for their passports. They did not look for drugs or turn anybody out of their caves.

Later that evening everyone was sitting round Mama's store as usual. Mama was Greek. She had grey hair and blue eyes. Her face was lined and white. Tonight she seemed very tired. She moved slowly backwards and forwards, cleaning out her shop, throwing down buckets of water. Watching Philippe and the others lounging on the beach, eating yoghurt, leaning against the ice-cream machine, it suddenly seemed extraordinary that they should be idle while Mama worked. If I had spoken Greek, and if the others had not been there, I might have offered to help her. As it was, I was as idle as the rest. Most of the young people who went past looked bored. An American with a face and body like a weasel meandered along, aimlessly throwing a stick to and fro. Two other boys sat against the wall drinking wine out of a plastic container – wine that was amazingly cheap, for them.

That night when I went to bed in my cave, I felt sad. I realized that in another month or so my life here, which was now everything, would be merely a collection of remembered images. One of these would be Philippe on the rocks at sunset with his long stick of bamboo, flinging his blond hair back, looking in the distance like a Scandinavian caveman.

I woke up with a strong sense that I had re-entered my child-hood during the night. I was again on the common in Berkshire in summer, among the poppies, with Jonathan. Everything was very safe.

Craig and Michael had now left. In the morning an American with a face like a piranha fish was in the square. He had been to the market in the local town.

He asked if anyone wanted to walk over the mountain with him to a beach where he was staying. I said I would. I helped him carry huge bags of his vegetables over the mountain path and put them down outside the stone beach house where he was staying.

This beach was enormously long, with miles of white sand. I said I would go for a walk up the beach on my own. As I rounded a bend, I saw three stationary tanks. Near the tanks were several American Marines with cropped hair. They were swimming in their trousers.

Then a young man came running out of a stone house under the trees. He rushed towards me over the hot sand, a blue towel tied round his head, like a parody of a Bedouin Arab.

'What on earth are the tanks doing here?' I asked. I noticed he was wearing pink lipstick.

'Oh, they've come from the American ship,' he said. 'They won't do any harm . . . I want some hash,' he continued. 'I've just taken some acid. Would you like to walk up the beach with me to the other house?'

I followed him back the way I had come. The seaweed felt like velvet under my feet.

At the other stone house, where I had left the vegetables, a group of people were already smoking hash from a chillum and eating salad. The fat American girl from Mátala was there. She had no clothes on and had swum over from Mátala. There was also a French girl, wearing new Greek clothes, who had just bought a donkey.

'I love donkeys,' the fat American girl said. 'Please bring your donkey to our village and bring him up to our cave.'

There was a commotion outside and two American Marines with cropped hair and enormously long legs walked in. One of them was black. He said they both came from Kentucky. They were offered some hash, but the white man said he preferred juice.

'This is the first time we've been allowed to swim since we arrived in the Mediterranean three weeks ago,' he told us.

Everyone except him became very stoned. At least three people, besides the man wearing pink lipstick, had taken acid.

I walked alone out of the house on to the beach. Two tanks were coming towards me, churning up sand with their wheels. I had never seen tanks close up before. More American Marines sat on top of them, with demented expressions. One, who was smoking a cigarette, winked. Then the tanks turned right, and drove slowly into the sea, where they seemed to become amphibious. They floated out to their big ship.

The man who looked like a piranha fish came out of the house and stood beside me.

'Most unpleasant,' I observed, pointing to the tanks.

'For them, you mean?'

'No, for us.'

The fat American girl joined us. 'It's extraordinary that they don't see,' she said, about the Marines.

I suddenly felt irritated with her, and with myself. Although I didn't like the tanks, I realized that we had no business feeling superior.

In this corner of a Cretan beach two sides of America met. We represented the joint-smoking, do-nothing, supposedly peace-loving hippies, who had all been able to pay our fares to Europe. The Marines, many of them young men from poor

146

families in the American South, were convenient symbols to us of an unpleasant warmongering society. But these young men had not had much choice. All of us, they and we, were probably just as bewildered as each other.

When I got back to Mátala, I went over to the Red Beach and swam. Philippe was there. He did not actually approach me, but sat on the rocks several yards away, looking at me between his legs and making faces.

The morning after I had met the Marines on the beach I went and made coffee in Ben's room. He stroked me and told me I was like a beautiful plant, and that I was mentally relaxed. I liked Ben, but he reminded me of an elderly woman, rather than a lover. He was comfortable and sympathetic.

I told Ben about the Marines and how my father had been in the navy for most of his life. He had not wanted to go into it, I explained, but had been sent to naval college aged twelve, by his father, an admiral. My father had recounted that on visiting days the young cadets, still only twelve or thirteen, were jeered at by the other boys if they were spotted kissing their mothers or sisters. My father, who was by nature physically demonstrative, had not expressed disapproval at this unthinking brutality when he told me this.

Ben said he would like to sculpt me later that day on the Red Beach, where he had hidden some clay in a cave. His room was filthy. The floor was covered with orange peel, empty tins, paper and cigarette butts. I threw some of these into the wastepaper basket. Ben was so lethargic that he obviously would not move for some time. I went to the Red Beach on my own.

Later Ben came and joined me on a rock. He stroked my back and said, 'Let's have a relationship. We like each other, you've got a good body, mine's not too bad, so let's have a relationship.'

What an insipid proposition, I thought.

Philippe was already on the beach with Monique, a Frenchwoman who had arrived that morning. I did not like her, because I thought she was unpleasantly tough and because I did not

147

trust her. She had a flat white face and little chestnut eyes. Her body could have been on the cover of a calendar with pictures showing 'sex kittens'. She reminded me of Brigitte Bardot in my father's books of photographs of the French starlet.

Monique had been in Mátala already, the week before I arrived, then had gone to Athens to look for work. There she had met a rich Greek man who had given her two thousand drachmas and all the food from his fridge. In return she had to be in his flat in Athens when he got back from his business trips. He was away on one now, so she had returned to Mátala.

When I saw Monique on the beach with Philippe, I realized I was jealous.

Ben was annoying me. I allowed him to sketch me by the rocks, then I moved away from him.

He said, 'You should overcome your inhibitions and have a relationship.'

I said, 'You've got no business to say I've got inhibitions just because I don't want to have a relationship with you.'

He then went back to the beach, offended. I looked at him with distaste.

When I returned to the beach from the rocks, Ben was sitting with Philippe and Monique. Philippe seemed pleased that I might be jealous. I went into the sea. Philippe called after me, inviting me to have some biscuits, but I refused.

At sunset I began climbing the cliff path on my own, to go back to the village. Philippe followed me. He climbed up a much steeper place, to show off. We then walked in single file, Philippe in front. As we neared the village, he stopped. He was wearing only his coffee-coloured bathing trunks.

'Why are you stopping?' I asked.

'I love you,' he replied. 'I'd like to throw myself over that cliff, to keep this memory intact. Do you understand?'

'Yes,' I said. I moved close to him. We walked the rest of the way back together. In the square some local Greek boys were playing football. Philippe joined them boisterously.

That night I slept with Philippe on the roof. There were

148

hundreds of stars. It was cold with only one sleeping-bag to cover us both. At midnight Philippe stole four ice-creams from a fridge outside Mama's shop. We ate them at once. Then Philippe boasted to me about being a misogynist. He said women were never as intelligent as men. He said they always married the man who gave them economic security.

'Why are you so keen to attack women?' I asked.

We made love in different positions. Philippe told me that he had once made love to Monique, but she didn't want him to do it again because he had hurt her. 'She says I make love like a brute.'

'But you like that, don't you?' I said. 'You think it's masculine.'

'Wouldn't you like to have a baby?' said Philippe. 'I'll make you a little baby with blond hair and blue eyes. We'll give it to my mother. She likes little boys. She's raised six of them.'

I did not like the idea of Philippe's mother looking after my baby. 'Is she French?' I said doubtfully.

'Yes.'

Philippe then tried to find out what I thought of him. 'Some people tell me my blond hair's pretty,' he said. 'But I know it's like straw. When it was shorter, it was darker.'

I stroked his beard. 'A beard's nice,' I said. 'It's erotic.'

'Yes, I think younger girls are impressed by a beard,' said Philippe.

I was thinking how vain he was. I did not mind, though. I felt touched.

'I hate almost everyone here,' said Philippe. 'You've got to make people respect you before they trample on you. That's why I'm proud.'

'But how do you know? You don't speak to them,' I said. 'You don't speak English. You must give people the benefit of the doubt.'

'Last year I had a friend here who I loved,' said Philippe. 'A French boy. He played the guitar, not like these American "*cons*", with their fake mysticism and their Hermann Hesse. He knew all that was shit. He had refused to go into the army and been put in prison because of it. There's no one like that for me this year.'

'What about Ben?' I said.

'It's not the same,' Philippe replied. 'If I left tomorrow, it would make no difference to him.' He added that he was 'profoundly a pessimist'. 'Le confort, c'est la merde!' He thought he would like to live in Scandinavia. 'There it is still possible to die of cold, or hunger. You can be alone with the elements. Hippies don't go there because they like the sun. And you, you're wicked. You want an American during the day and a Frenchman at night.'

We found a blond hair on my stomach.

'Ah, an American's hair,' said Philippe.

'Don't be ridiculous.'

The next night we walked out to the Mermaid Café. There was no bean soup left. Instead we had spaghetti and salad.

Philippe liked the young Greek waiters. 'At least they have their heads screwed on, not like those "*con*" Americans,' he said, pointing to the other people eating.

'They're not all American anyway,' I said. 'At that table there's a Greek and a Spaniard.'

'He may be Greek, but he lives in America,' said Philippe.

He invited the young waiter to compete with him and see who could get whose arm on to the table first. The Greek boy won. (His arm was shorter so his friend helped him.) Philippe became very excited and angry. 'You're not allowed to help!' he shouted.

Another waiter brought us some brandy. The Greeks all said, '*Yassas!*' and drank it in one gulp. Another little Greek boy, who was eating at the same table and who obviously admired Philippe, began making faces.

'He's fourteen, but he already knows how to make obscene gestures,' said Philippe. Then he became pensive. His yellow-brown eyes looked dreamy. 'You'll be getting some money from England perhaps?' he said.

'No, I won't,' I replied.

'How will you get back?'

150

'I don't know. I shall stay a bit longer.'

'That's good.'

He stroked my leg under the table. Suddenly all the lights went out.

'Let's quickly take the money of all the Americans here!' said Philippe.

Everyone seemed to dislike Americans, including my father. I remembered how, in London, Ian and I had seen a documentary film in which American soldiers, back from Vietnam, had 'confessed' to some of their barbaric behaviour during the Vietnam War, when they said they had taken pleasure in killing or torturing 'geeks' (their name for the Vietnamese). They had repented, in what I thought was an embarrassingly sentimental way. Ian, like some of these young men, had sobbed as he watched the film. (He had also sobbed when a Polish musician had played the violin over our table in a nightclub during the skiing holiday on which I had met him and Carla.) I had been brought up to admire courage. I thought of a story my mother had told me about my father. They had been in a plane which had just landed at Athens Airport. My mother had looked out of the window and seen that one of the engines was on fire. She had alerted my father, who was doing the *Times* crossword. My father said he had already noticed the fire, several minutes earlier.

'They'll put it out,' he told my mother, continuing with the crossword.

My father had spent four challenging years on the North Atlantic, commanding destroyers. A cousin of my mother had observed that, despite his bravery, my father's nerves had been 'completely shattered' by the experience. Perhaps this was why my father now seemed unable to concentrate or make proper conversation and why he yelled orders at us all the time, like 'Pipe down!'

This same cousin had sent her son to stay with us for a weekend when he was a teenager. 'He said your father shouted orders all the time, but no one took any notice,' she told me later, when I saw her in London.

I felt angry, but said nothing. I knew it was true, and that my father in some ways was seen as a slightly ridiculous larger-than-life figure, but I also knew that there had been a time in his life when people *had* taken notice of him, when they had had to, a time when he had saved lives.

The following morning I set off to drink tea with Ben as usual. It was impossible as he was in bed with a witch. The witch was a girl from Scandinavia. She had red hair, plucked eyebrows and a wardrobe of velvet clothes. She carried a bottle of wine permanently with her. Wherever she walked she left a cloud of cheap perfume. She had a dozen bracelets on each arm and a tattoo of the devil across her chest.

Philippe was extremely sceptical about Ben sleeping with the witch. Later, when we were on the Red Beach, he said that Ben always made love to monsters. Lola, the Hare Krishna chanter, was a monster too, said Philippe.

'But monsters also want to make love,' I pointed out.

Philippe said he was anti-contraceptives. 'Wouldn't you like a baby?' he urged again. 'It would be a companion for you. In five years you'd have a little boy to play chess with.'

We stood together on the rocks and he talked about his family. 'I love my grandfather,' he said. 'He always gives me money. He's very intellectual. He used to be an engineer. He does the crossword even now, to keep his brain working. My grand-mother's strict, though. She's never liked me. I used to stick my tongue out at her when I was little. I was a savage.' He showed me a scar on his leg where his younger brother had attacked him with a knife. 'He's intelligent but unstable,' he said. He could have got good results at school, but there was nowhere at home to do his homework. 'The house is always so full. I do the cooking. My mother hates doing it. She's ill all the time. She suffers from her nerves.'

I'm not surprised, I thought.

We discussed Sartre. Philippe said another of his brothers worked on the railways and was a member of the Communist Party. 'There are a lot of strikes on the railways,' he said. 'I hope you'll come and see me in Alsace-Lorraine.' Then he sprang back over the rocks to the beach.

Next day Philippe took me for a walk in the mountains. First we went to see some Canadians, who had parked their van a mile out of the village. Rick was a painter. He and his 'old lady', Naomi, had made their van very cosy. They had cooking facilities, water and a foam mattress. Stuck on the walls were two photographs of themselves as a loving couple. Naomi was a serene girl with two long plaits and a sweet expression, like a little cat. She was consistently strict with Rick, as if she were his parent. As he went through all his sketch pads, showing portraits of old Greek men, wild flowers, sunsets and nudes, she reprimanded him. 'They must be bored by now.'

While I continued looking at the sketches, Philippe went and sat in the front of the van and talked to Naomi.

Afterwards he told me he had made love to her twice, before I arrived in Mátala. 'She likes me,' he said. 'She also made love with a friend of mine, Pierre, and a lot of other men too. Pierre and I laughed.'

He led me up to a little chapel in the mountains. Here there was a spring of fresh water and beautiful pink plants. Inside were pictures of the saints, including one of St George killing the dragon.

'There's an English saint in there,' I told Philippe.

'Don't be stupid. The saints have no nationality.'

He made me take off my clothes and we made love on the rocks outside. Then I read him a letter I had had from my father that morning, which had arrived at Mama's store. 'He says, "Don't make love to Frenchmen",' I teased.

For a few moments Philippe believed it. He looked hurt. 'He doesn't really, does he?'

Then he began to cross-question me about why I had stayed so long in Mátala after going with Craig to Phaistós that day.

'I don't know,' I said. 'Why should I know? I hate these questions. You want me to say I stayed because of you.'

'Well, what do you think of me?' Philippe persisted.

'You just want different girls' opinions of you to flatter your vanity,' I said. 'I'm not going to flatter you.'

Philippe leaped up. 'Let's make love every hundred yards till we get back to Mátala,' he said.

We made love again on the mountain. There seemed to be no one for miles around. I had a memory of the train going through my grandmother's valley. I felt very peaceful. We saw an enormous dark-grey serpent near Rick's van, among the pop-corn shells.

As it was Sunday, over fifty Greek tourists were on the beach. Philippe began frying potatoes in Ben's room then disappeared. I lay on Ben's bed, nearly asleep. A New Yorker, who had just arrived in Mátala, came in. He had short hair and seemed nervy and intolerant. He had had a quarrel with some Germans on the boat coming to Iráklion. 'They were like a pack of wolves, those Huns. A pack of wolves.'

He asked me what my parents were like.

'My father used to be a naval commander,' I said.

'Ah, the Royal Navy, eh?' He went on, 'I have no respect for hippies. They're idle and commonplace. They have third-rate brains. They ruin their nervous system with drugs. They have no courage. When I was in Israel, I ran six miles along the beach every day. I believe in discipline.'

He showed me a letter he had written to a Greek astrologer. 'Do you think that should induce him to meet me?' he said.

The letter was long and complicated. In it he spoke of his life being 'a tragic waste'. He said he had been greatly influenced by Neptune and often felt guided by an inner voice. 'Without a desire for self-aggrandizement, I must honestly say that I have spent many hours in libraries reading the classics,' the letter said.

'I'm asking you to criticize the letter,' he explained. 'I can see you have the mind of a genius.'

Unfortunately this flattery was ruined by the entrance of Rick, whom Philippe and I had visited that afternoon. Within a couple of minutes the New Yorker had told Rick that he also had the mind of a genius. The two of them began talking about the so-called witch.

'I think she's possessed by the devil,' said the New Yorker.

'She's too open for that,' I said. 'There's no harm in her.'

'That kind of thing's rubbish anyway,' said Rick. 'In the end nothing matters. I've seen many people die.'

'Die of drugs, I suppose,' said the New Yorker sharply. 'I cannot accept that philosophy.'

'You remind me of a girl back home,' Rick told me. 'Carol McBride. She has the same manner. She also wants something more than other people. She keeps it hidden. She wants it bad, but she doesn't really know what it is. That's like you.'

'Perhaps,' I said. 'Yes, you're right. How do you know?'

'I watch people,' said Rick.

Outside I glimpsed Philippe with a girl who looked like Princess Anne.

'That Frenchman likes to tickle girls' butts,' said the New Yorker.

Philippe came in, wearing a windcheater that was too small for him and a white handkerchief tied round his head. I thought he had dressed up for me.

'You look quite different in that *bandeau*,' I said.

'You stay in this room tonight,' he told me.

'I don't want to make love with Ben,' I said.

'I'm leaving you here with him,' said Philippe. 'That's what I did before. I told him, "You can have her." He's my friend.'

I obediently went to sleep in Ben's bed. It was very comfortable, but full of sand. After midnight there was a knock on the door. It was the witch.

'Can I sleep on the floor in my sleeping-bag?' she asked.

I felt sorry for her. I thought she must be lonely. 'Of course,' I said. 'I don't know if Ben is coming back tonight. Perhaps you could sleep in the other bed.'

The witch stretched out on the floor and fell into a sound sleep. After an hour Ben returned. He looked at we two prostrate girls.

'Well, I've had these two, but I'll have them again,' he murmured.

I pretended to be asleep.

While I was making cinnamon tea in Ben's room the next day, I realized it was idiotic to have slept there. Ben was determined to make love to me again.

'He's annoyed because he thought you were an easy lay,' said Philippe, who had turned up there in the morning as usual. He began romping with me on the bed. When he left, Ben grabbed hold of me, but I pulled away. He criticized me for having a complex about sex. This made me really angry.

'Because I don't want to sleep with you, because your male vanity's been hurt, you want to make out there's something wrong with me,' I said.

'I haven't got much male vanity,' said Ben sulkily. He said he was going to write a poem about how women preferred men who were horrible to them.

'Yes, that's quite true,' I said.

Philippe and two other French boys and I were asked to do some gardening for the man who owned the only hotel in Mátala. He had another restaurant a few miles from the village, and some fields of tomatoes. He promised to pay us a hundred drachmas each for helping with the tomatoes.

He was very generous about feeding us. In the morning he drove us out to the restaurant and gave us white cheese and bread and wine. Then he led us outside, and gave us four axes. My axe was smaller than anyone else's, presumably because I was a girl. Our Greek employer wanted us to loosen the earth around the tomato plants, which were only about a foot high. He showed us how to do it. Philippe was the best. He caught on very quickly. He was also strong.

I chopped off several tomato plants by mistake. Our boss walked angrily up and down my row, shaking his head and muttering, *'Kaput! Kaput!'*

'You're a disaster for his tomatoes,' said Philippe.

Then the man went back inside his house.

The three French boys immediately sat down and embarked on a philosophical discussion about the nature of work. I particularly liked one boy. He had bushy brown hair. He said he had left university to work in a factory. I could not be sure whether this was a political gesture or not.

'Did you get good pay?' I asked.

'No. Not in France,' he said. 'The bosses are terrible.'

'Were there strikes?'

'Yes.'

'What did you have to do?'

The boy said he had managed some kind of wheel.

The other boy, who was a Parisian, did not like our digging work. 'Fancy wasting your life doing this kind of slogging,' he said. 'Six hours pass without your knowing. I hate these routine jobs.'

Philippe kept mocking me for not doing it properly. He was determined that, being female, I should not know how to do it. I was sure that he would have criticized me equally for doing it conscientiously.

After a couple of hours the Greek man came out again. He wore a handkerchief tied round his head, to protect it from the sun. His four-year-old son, who also had a handkerchief round his head, came with him. The man inspected our work. He said Philippe was the best. Then he invited us all in for lunch.

The restaurant, which was called Dionysius, was spacious, with light-green walls, a television and a couple of obscene calendars. The man gave us thick potato omelette, and more cheese and wine. Then he said we could have an hour's rest.

We went outside and lay in the long grass. Philippe sprang on top of me. I found this humiliating, in front of the French boy whom I admired. We all went to sleep in the sun and woke up covered with grass seed.

In the afternoon we did some more work in the tomato field. Philippe and the other boys spent a great deal of time sitting down and talking. At five the Greek man's other son, who was about nineteen, came and did some raking beside us. As he spoke some French, the French boy with bushy hair, who'd worked in a factory, started a conversation with him. 'It's difficult for us to work because we aren't used to it,' he explained to the Greek boy. 'We only work to eat. We think people who work are mad.'

I liked this French boy, because he was independent and energetic. He seemed much more mature than Philippe. He wanted to live his own life, but this did not mean he was nihilistic. He said he found Mátala debilitating. There was too much drug talk. He was leaving.

Philippe and I were supposed to work again the next day, with the tomatoes, but we overslept on the roof. I decided I, like the French boy, wanted to quit Mátala. I walked round the square, asking people for a lift to Iráklion.

'I'm going today or tomorrow,' I told Philippe.

He shrugged. He sat on the roof hiding his face in his hair.

'Are you going on to the Arab countries?' I asked him.

'I don't know.'

He went off towards the beach, carrying a blanket and a copy of Plato.

'I'll come later,' I said.

He nodded.

I sat on our roof reading an old copy of *Mad* magazine I had picked up. Mátala was nearly empty, I realized. Suddenly it seemed stagnant. I knew Philippe didn't want me to go. I ran over the mountains to the Red Beach. He was lying on his blanket. I thought he had been crying. I took him in my arms. We made love. Then I swam. Philippe retreated to a shady part of the rocks, reading Plato.

I could not make up my mind whether to go or not. Mátala seemed already to belong to my past. There was nothing more for me to do there. A new lot of people would soon arrive. I did not want to have to make friends with them.

It was very hot on the Red Beach. Philippe and I made love again in a small cove further away, which was full of tar.

When the sun got lower, we went back to the Red Beach and

Philippe began to tease me. He called Ben, who was sunbathing near some German girls. We all three lay together on a blanket. Philippe told us more stories about his younger brother, who, he said, was notorious for drinking and seducing girls.

'He's famous for miles around where we live,' said Philippe.

'My brother's also an alcoholic,' I said idiotically.

'But not like mine,' Philippe boasted.

He and Ben took it in turns to pretend to rape me. After a while I grew angry. I put on my clothes and walked up the mountain. Philippe came after me.

'You're not angry, are you?' he said. 'Yes, you are. Good. It gives you character... Are you really leaving tomorrow?'

I noticed again how beautiful the coast was.

I went and sat in the square. The witch came and sat beside me. She smelled bad.

'I was drunk yesterday,' said the witch. 'I think I'll go and buy another bottle of retsina. Perhaps that'll make me better.' She laughed ruefully.

'Why do you drink?' I asked.

The witch did not answer. She rose and walked across the square, dragging her long skirts. People said she slept with locals as well as hippies. I thought that she was more vulnerable than the other young in Mátala. Sometimes she would rush round the village giving out presents – sticks of incense, or biscuits. I was indignant that she was shunned. Hippies professed to follow the philosophy of 'do your own thing', but as soon as they met someone really beyond the pale, they didn't like them.

Later Philippe and I sat in the café, under very bright electric light. Philippe tried to teach me chess.

'Tu n'as pas de morale,' he said.

'What does that mean?' I said. It meant that I didn't care about winning.

Philippe played instead with a French boy, whose girlfriend came to watch. She had cropped hair and an intelligent face. She told us that her father was afraid of the Arabs in Paris. 'He has a big lock on his front door,' she said. 'He is extremely rich.'

Later, on the roof, Philippe came and bounced on top of me as though I were a horse. He was in high spirits.

'I've just stolen twelve ice-creams,' he said.

'You'll overreach yourself. I hate making love on the roof,' I added. 'It's so cold.'

I dreamed that I looked for Philippe everywhere. I decided that he couldn't have gone to the beach; it was too rough. I was desperately afraid that Monique, the French girl, might be with him, but she wasn't. Then I went looking on the beaches myself. I went for miles. I was wearing my grandmother's coat.

When Philippe woke up next morning, he said '*Merde*' several times. 'I dreamed in the night all my friends were dead,' he told me. 'Are you really going today?'

'I think so,' I said.

Later I went down to the Red Beach. I realized I was very bored. Philippe and I made half-hearted love on the rock.

'I think I should leave,' I said.

'You could catch the bus now if you hurry,' he said.

We ran up the mountain. The bus was still in the square.

'Give your paperbacks to me. Perhaps I can sell them.'

'Two of them are Ben's,' I said.

Philippe came to the bus with me. He carried my bag. He looked young and gangling standing there in his bathing trunks.

The witch was also on the bus. She said she was going to the hospital in Moíres. 'I want someone to come with me,' she said. 'I'm frightened.'

'Don't talk to the witch,' Philippe advised me. 'When will you come to France?'

'Later this summer,' I said. 'It's easy for me to go to Paris,' I added.

'Well, my home isn't all that far from there,' said Philippe. He winked. 'Do you want me to get you something to eat?'

'A yoghurt.' I passed him ten drachmas. Philippe bought one for himself as well. Then the bus left.

I let the witch get off the bus at Moíres on her own.

A few days later I was on a night-train from Rome to Paris.

From Paris I would return to London. That night I had two admirers, both Italian, the ticket collector and a man from Interpol. The ticket collector said he was a member of the Communist Party in Italy. He asked me if I liked making love.

I said, 'I don't talk about that to strangers.'

'I'm not a stranger,' he replied. 'My name's Giorgio.'

'I want to be alone in this railway carriage,' I said. 'If you don't leave me, I'll have to go and sit with those women next door.'

He looked startled. 'All right, just give me your hand.'

The man from Interpol was more subtle. He chanted 'Bella ragazza!' at me, and said that women should be wooed gently. He told me I had beautiful eyes. 'Let's put on the blue light,' he said. 'It's more romantic.'

'No, blue light not good,' I replied, in pidgin English.

He pinched my cheek several times, saying, *'Ciao!'*

'Ciao!' I replied.

'Were you in love in Greece?' he asked. 'What was his name?'

'Philippe.'

'Filippo! And now, when you reach the frontier, it will just be a good memory.'

He went on crooning at me, looking like a little gnome.

Claude

It was August and I was back in London. Carla, her drama course over, had followed Ian to Los Angeles, where, unable to get acting work, she had become a waitress. Ian had had to give up his job after only three days. His employer, although he had advertised for a non-gay young man, had designs on Ian. Ian was now selling liquor in Beverly Hills.

My father begged me to join him on holiday in Mallorca, where he was staying alone in a rented house. My mother was driving out later. It was now two months since I had returned from Crete. I had just finished a temporary job for a publisher in Covent Garden, contributing to a children's encyclopedia.

'You can swim and sunbathe here as much as you like and have delicious food,' wrote my father, trying to tempt me.

My father came to meet me, alone, at Palma Airport. I saw him waiting for me beyond customs. He was in a white shirt and cream trousers, and looked foreign, relaxed and glamorous. Was Europe, rather than England, really his natural habitat? I wondered again. I knew that as a boy he had enjoyed holidays with his French cousins at La Baule, whereas his sister had once told me she had hated these visits. My father also liked sophisticated foreign food.

When I came out of customs, my father kissed me tenderly on the cheek. For the first time I had an inkling of what my father might be like as a lover – softer and more tender than his brusque manners and shouting might at first convey.

As we drove the hour and a half to the rented house in the hills, my father seemed to have difficulty in keeping the car straight. Several times, soon after leaving the airport, we hit the kerb on the side of the road. When I complained, he retorted, 'Well, it's much better than hitting another car, isn't it?'

My parents had rented the same house the year before, and the Spanish manservant, José, who worked there, seemed very fond of my father.

Despite having written to me about the delights of swimming and sunbathing, my father, as he did at home, actually spent most of his time in bed, except when he sat on the veranda drinking anis or went swimming – he only stayed in for a few minutes – in the beautiful blue curved swimming pool.

My father had had two more operations on the area surrounding his now non-existent appendix, and as a result his heavily scarred stomach hung over the top of his bathing pants. He often dived into the pool with a terrible belly-flop, but this didn't appear to cause him any pain. I was fearful that his stomach would split open.

As he sat on the veranda drinking anis, my father usually did the *Times* crossword of two days earlier, or read a novel. Sometimes he scribbled illegible notes to himself in the margins. In a novel by Molly Parkin I saw that he had written: 'Amusing, but depraved.'

From the veranda he would shout orders to José, to bring ice, olives or his hearing-aid from upstairs. Each morning, when José was in the village shopping, my father would get exasperated that he had not returned and shout, 'What the bloody hell is he doing in there?'

My father did not make proper conversation with me at meals (served by José in a white jacket), but seemed to want to get through them as quickly as possible. Sometimes he would make comments about the other English people staying near by. 'Your cousin Daisy never stops talking! Pap pap pap pap! I call her La Mitroyeuse . . . Lucy's an adventuress. She's living on money left to her by two men.'

Lucy, aged eighty, liked my father, and he liked her. (She had been friends with both the Duchess of Windsor and one of the king's former mistresses. Lucy, like my father, did the *Times* crossword every day, or tried to. Also, she wasn't afraid of my father, as many people were.)

My father had managed to borrow a typewriter for me, from a woman called Mrs Percival. Two days after I arrived, when my father was due to go to Mrs Percival's for dinner, we received news that she had died earlier that day, choking to death at her own lunch table.

My father reacted to this by saying to me accusingly, again and again, 'Well, *you're* all right! You've got her typewriter!' Lucy, who had been there when Mrs Percival had choked to death, came to lunch with us the day after. At first Lucy was on her best behaviour. She was wearing white – white trousers and a pure white jumper which she had crocheted herself. After about fifteen minutes she declared, 'I want my lunch!'

My father replied, 'You'll get it when it's ready.'

While Lucy and I sipped white wine, I argued with Lucy about my father. I said he criticized members of his club for being 'Middle European upstarts' or 'dagos' (despite his own foreign blood), then got annoyed when these people, hoping to get a leg-up in English 'society', tried to conceal their origins.

My father was sitting scowling at us. He couldn't hear much because his hearing-aid had been eaten by José's dog the night before.

A storm was brewing. We watched the storm clouds crowd over the mountains. The mountains were grey already; the dark clouds made them black. Lucy said the storm made her think of 'The Ride of the Valkyries'.

Lucy said, 'Now, let's see what your father *does* like . . . He admires men who fought well in the war.'

I was secretly impressed by the way Lucy defended my father and, after she had argued with me, I began to like her.

After lunch she said she had to go, to feed her wild kittens, which she had found abandoned on the mountain above her house. She was feeding them regularly with a fountain-pen filler.

When my mother arrived, Lucy asked us to a drinks party at her house by the sea.

Drinks were served on a small veranda covered with purple bougainvillea. The Swiss ambassador to Moscow was sitting

164

on the balcony. He introduced me to his son, who was about my age and had skinny white legs, a pouting mouth and spectacles. I asked what he did, and he said he was about to take the Foreign Office exams. I was going to question him further when my father butted in. The Swiss ambassador's son left me and went and stood by a wall, looking ill at ease.

On this holiday my father was possessive of me and my mother. She and I met a charming Swedish man, a vegetarian who had lived in Peru, at a party given by our cousin Daisy. My mother and I both liked blond men and found him romantic. My mother nicknamed him Thor, after the Nordic god, and suggested that we ask him to dinner. My father was furious. He said that Thor looked very unstable and was far too thin. He wouldn't be surprised either if he had 'been in a looney bin'.

After two weeks on the island I began to get restless. I didn't want to return to Hackney now that Ian and Carla had left. I decided to let the house and go to France. I thought vaguely that I might even visit Philippe in Alsace-Lorraine, but first I would go to Paris.

My grandmother didn't want me to go abroad. She wanted me to stay near her. I told my father this. He was already annoyed with my grandmother for inviting her American niece to stay, with a married Englishman with whom she was having an affair. 'Your grandmother is condoning immorality!' he declared.

Back in London I received a letter from him: 'Your grandmother is very lazy and very spoiled. It was her fault that Jonathan died. Of course you should go to Paris.'

A week later I took the ferry to France, carrying my orange portable typewriter and a bag of clothes.

I entered the flat in Paris on a late summer's day. The walls in the kitchen were bright blue; everywhere were posters of cats. The boy who opened the door was English; he had shallow green eyes and he was wearing bathing pants.

'Are Simone and Anthony here?' I asked.

'They're on holiday.'

'Well, they said I could crash here, if I couldn't find anywhere else.'

The boy leered, and tottered sideways. He was stoned. I didn't like him. His girlfriend, wearing a yellow bikini over her pink thighs, stood behind him. She at least was smiling.

'There are some French people in the next room,' said the boy. 'You could ask them. They live here.'

I knocked on the door. A tall boy, with a pale face and flared nostrils like a blood horse, came out.

'*Oui, oui*, you can stay here. The key is under the mat always.'

The English boy was now standing on the balcony of the kitchen. 'Where do you come from? London?' he asked.

'Yes.'

'This is a nice flat, if they did it up,' he said awkwardly, thus revealing his idea of how a flat should not be. It shouldn't have a stone floor and be filled with dust. It shouldn't have no curtains.

'But Simone and Anthony like it like this,' I said.

The next day I moved in. The English couple left, to go grape-picking. I put my bag and portable typewriter into the small room next to the kitchen. It had light-green walls. There was a tiny chest of drawers, more posters of cats, a tartan mattress and shelves filled with bottles of laxatives.

The French couple living there seemed weird and unfriendly. They were called Claude and Colette. At first, when I met Colette in the kitchen, I thought she was a junkie. This was because she trembled and her big eyes moved from side to side. She was also very thin. She looked as if she would break, like a puppet made of wood.

'*Ou est la chiotte?*' I asked that afternoon. Colette didn't understand. She seemed scared.

'*Ou est la chiotte?*' I said again. I stared at Colette's thin arms to see if there were any marks to show she had been shooting heroin. But there was nothing.

Then Colette understood. She led me to the door of the flat and pointed to another door on the staircase.

The lavatory was tiny. There was hardly room for one's legs.

Staring me in the face as I sat there was a gigantic colour photo of a cat. Anthony, who lived in the flat, was obsessed with cats. I did not like them.

When I came out of the lavatory and into the flat, Colette had disappeared into another room. There was an atmosphere of tension in the flat. It gave me a pain in my stomach.

That evening was worse. When I went into the kitchen, which was dimly lit, Colette was lying on the sofa. She leaped up, with an expression of terror and hate, and ran into the next room. I cooked an omelette, feeling isolated.

Later Claude came back. He had a pale, agonized face, with shadows under his eyes. When he saw me, he put one hand theatrically to his head, moaned, '*J'ai mal à la tête!*' and staggered out of the kitchen.

I went to ask Colette if I could put on the radio. She was sitting at a desk wearing a black and white Moroccan cape.

'*Bien sûr,*' she said. She looked at me with malice.

The next evening, as we two sat at the kitchen table among the dirty plates, old newspapers and dried flowers, waiting for Claude to come home, Colette told me about the birth of her son three years ago.

It was dreadful; she was in labour for twelve hours. The doctors were cruel; when the baby's head emerged it wouldn't go any further, and they told her she wasn't trying. But she was pushing so hard she thought she would break.

After she told me this, we became friends.

I had been in the flat ten days. On the fifth day Allende had been assassinated. On the ninth day Colette left, to go to a sleep clinic near Toulouse.

The weather had got colder. In my room there was a note from Colette. '*Claude te donne le manteau.*' There was Claude's cream-coloured coat, lined with sheep's wool, on my mattress.

I met Claude in the kitchen.

'You'll need this coat when it's really cold,' I said, holding it out.

'I have another,' he said. He picked up a blue jacket from the chair. He put his long arms into the sleeves. 'See, this is wool,' he said. 'Very warm.'

I wanted the coat, but I didn't want to take it if Claude needed it. 'I'll give it back when I get my own coat from England,' I said.

I poured myself out a bowl of muesli. 'Do you want some?'

Claude shook his head. He sat down at the table.

'Did Colette go happily to the clinic?' I asked.

Claude nodded.

'I wouldn't like a cure like that,' I said. 'The sleep cure.'

'Why not?'

'It's too much like death.'

'I'm tired,' said Claude, and disappeared into his dark room, probably to sleep. He wanted to live in his own world of dreams. He wanted to produce plays. But he had to look after Colette and his son in Toulouse. Their son, now three, was staying with Colette's parents.

'Are you cut off from your family?' I had asked the other night.

'Almost completely.'

Now I was alone with Claude.

When I woke in the mornings, he woke at the same time. In the evenings I waited for him to come home. One night when he came home late, I felt like a child whose parents had deserted it. I even shed a few tears. Just before I met him, when I had made the decision to come to Paris, I had had the illusion that for the first time I was controlling my own life, in the way other people seemed to.

The morning after he came home late I felt very hungry, but there was only instant coffee. I had made one abortive attempt to get a job as an au pair with a woman called Madame Le Petit, who had two little boys. She wanted someone to teach them English. I had seen the ad in the *Herald Tribune* and gone for an interview. After showing me a tiny room with no hot water, Madame Le Petit had said rather desperately, 'I can count on you?' but I had never heard from her again. I decided to walk to the American Express and send a letter to my bank in London asking for fifty pounds.

I felt unexpectedly tired walking through the streets, probably because I hadn't eaten. Many people going to work had pained, stretched expressions on their faces. When I reached the Tuileries, it was with relief. The trees were already brown in this early autumn. I went to a kiosk and bought a banana for a franc. I remembered that they gave you energy. The people in the kiosk were still getting it ready for the day's customers. Perhaps it would not be bad to work in a park.

Around the place Vendôme the streets took on a different atmosphere. The air was filled with different Parisian scents. A woman stood outside Cartier's jeweller with her small son. They were looking at a brooch of a black and white leopard.

'That costs more than your father's house,' said the woman.

It was obvious that this thought titillated her. She did not want to steal the leopard, she wanted to be able to walk into that shop and buy it as if it were her right. On the other side of the street was a shop selling sleek leather handbags. There was a mystique attached to such expensive objects. They seemed almost religious, so out of reach were they from most people. Yet as soon as you were able to buy one, this mystique vanished.

Anthony and Simone returned to Paris. They said I could stay on in the flat as long as I wanted. Claude was leaving, as he had found somewhere to stay near his new job, moving scenery at the theatre at Châtelet.

Anthony and Simone, whom I had met in a London pub, two years earlier, were pale and gentle. Anthony's life, for eight months of the year, was lived in the night. He preferred the dark womb of his bedroom to the outside world. He was gaunt, with a bony face, a prominent nose and big grey eyes. Cafés and restaurants where he sometimes ate cheap food were painful to him, he said. He felt too exposed. He was afraid of strangers.

Sometimes he sat up all night typing and went to bed at dawn; at other times he drank in bars in the Latin Quarter. Only when he was drunk could he talk casually to strangers, he said. The rest of the time he could talk only on an intense level.

He had left Toronto five years earlier. He thought it a soulless city where everybody was too comfortable and too good. Life was too easy there, he said; it lacked passion, fury and fear. He had been raised by his grandmother in Canada. She adored cats. Now, in this flat in the Marais (the old marshlands of Paris), he stuck posters of cats all over the walls, to remind himself of her.

The only job he had ever had had been in the post office in Toronto, when he went back there one Christmas to see his grandmother. In Paris he didn't work. His grandmother sent him a hundred francs a week. He ate once a day, usually out, often couscous, which was very cheap. He bought *Le Monde*, *Libération* and the *New York Review of Books* and read them thoroughly.

His own writing was a kind of poetic prose monologue with few conversations.

Simone, unlike Anthony, had a job. She worked for a publisher of art books and art magazines. She talked about her boss disparagingly as 'this rich guy'. She had worked for him for eight years.

Simone had met Anthony at a 'happening' at the American University in Paris. Aged twenty, he had just arrived from Toronto and had been wandering about Paris on his own, drinking in cafés and carrying a copy of *Under the Volcano*. He told me that Simone had 'saved' him.

At first they had lived together in a series of cheap hotels and had once been gassed by the French police in a demonstration. Later Simone had bought this flat in the Marais, with family money.

Her family were French Protestants. Simone was beautiful with a white skin, large blue eyes and pale hair. She was kind and allowed people such as Claude and Colette and now me to live in the flat. She wanted to be generous.

Simone wore loose-fitting trousers and old black T-shirts and no make-up. She seemed to live on pumpkin seeds, black coffee and wine. Occasionally there was a bowl of bananas on the kitchen table. She and Anthony hardly went out together. He was asleep all day while she worked; when she returned, after a dance class, he was often out for his evening's drinking.

Once, referring to a smart dinner party she had attended with her father, a retired professor, Simone cried, 'I never want to be served from the left again!'

Kurt, an American friend of Anthony who was visiting, said, 'You're selling yourself short.'

And in a way she was, living on the margins of life out of a scrupulous desire not to be greedy and self-seeking – gentle blonde Simone, a child of the moon.

Claude had moved out and was staying with a friend. But he still had a key. He arrived at three one afternoon when Anthony was asleep and Simone was working. He took a shower and put on a red jersey. He had got very thin in the face, I thought. He sat on the sofa where I was typing and began to read me a letter Colette had sent from the south.

'She says that everyone in the clinic is mad. They go there to get well and stay for ever. The doctors treat them abominably. When she left the clinic and saw the lights of Toulouse, she burst into tears. The doctor wrote that down in his book.'

He had a peculiar childish expression that reminded me of my brother Luke, who had also been deprived of motherly affection. I wondered whether he would lie to me.

'You've got very thin since last week,' I said. 'At any rate, since Colette was here.'

'I've had nothing to eat, because I sent her all my money,' he said.

'Well, you can have a banana,' I said crossly.

Claude said it was his birthday the next day, and that he had a twin sister. I gave him ten francs, telling him to send flowers to her. I felt that he wanted to be bullied and told what to do. Again he reminded me of my brother.

I took him into my bedroom to give him the money.

Outside the pigeons sat on the grey streaked walls, in a row.
'They're ugly,' I said, about the pigeons.
'Like old women, don't you think so?' said Claude.

It was Claude's birthday party. I had bought him a pineapple.
I wondered whether to wear a dress. Then I decided not to,
because I didn't want him to think I was doing it for him. Simone,
however, put on a mauve shawl.

He arrived after midnight from the theatre, very extrovert.
He shook hands with all of us. Kurt, Anthony's New York friend,
was also there. Anthony gave Claude his birthday present. It
was a paper snake, made in China. It was extremely realistic.

Claude said, 'You've chosen well, Anthony. You've understood me. I have a son, but I'm a child myself. This snake can
do for both of us.' Then he played with the snake on the floor,
making it rear its head at both me and Simone. Soon we had all
drunk a great deal of hot red wine. I was drinking mine in a
bowl instead of a glass. I was sitting on the sofa, wearing a red
jersey and jeans.

Anthony said, 'You and Claude are both wearing red. That's
the colour for nonconformists. The people in red are always
shot first in a revolution.'

I said, 'I always wear red.'

Claude was sitting at Simone's feet, facing me. He described
to us how he had been rude to everyone at the theatre that
night. He had stood before one of the actors and torn the petals
off a flower, saying this symbolized the man's career. Then he
had argued with a Spanish actress who had complained about
him because he was only a *machiniste*. We all laughed.

Claude went into my room and put on his sackcloth shirt.
He came back into the kitchen and made swaying movements
with his body. I felt that the room was divided in half; Simone
and Claude understood the dance while Kurt and Anthony were
being North American and talking about popcorn. I was an
outsider. Claude's movements were fluid. He was neither man
nor woman.

Then he said he was going to leave. He kept hugging Simone. He came up to me where I was sitting on the sofa and said, 'I would like to fuck you.'

Then he kissed me chastely on the cheek, softly, like a child. Across the room I saw Simone's eyes fill with tears. Then Claude left.

I went into my room and switched off the light. I imagined what it would be like making love with Claude. Next door I could hear them talking. I thought Kurt was jealous of Claude. The men said something about his being a Latin lover.

Anthony said, 'He's married, for Christ's sake. He's done everything the wrong way round. He's got a wife and baby, then he had an affair with a much older woman.' He added, 'Only an insane person would come to this house.'

I thought I heard Kurt shouting, 'Honey!' to me. I put on Claude's sheepskin coat over my nightdress and went into the kitchen. I stood swaying by the door, as if, Anthony commented, my world were turning upside down.

Anthony remarked, 'You're wearing Claude's coat.'

I replied, 'It's my coat now.'

Kurt was shouting, 'Honey!' out of the window to someone in the house opposite. It was the girlfriend of a Dutchman whom he met regularly in a bar in the Latin Quarter. We all thought this woman was extremely bourgeois. This was because we saw her nearly every evening and morning and afternoon in the window putting on make-up. This was all she seemed to do.

Anthony asked me if I had read his friend Patrick's story about an old lady and a cat. I said I thought it was too lavatorial.

Anthony said, 'But Patrick's not from a bourgeois background. His father was a docker in San Francisco. Maybe your reaction's bourgeois.'

'Possibly,' I said.

Then Anthony said something about the English being puritanical.

I said, 'Well, I'm not. My parents may not be working class, but they're certainly not puritanical.'

Then I went back to bed. The others played records late into the night. In the morning I thought about Claude and how he had said, 'I would like to fuck you.' I was pleased he had said this. I felt close to him.

The next day, in Anthony and Simone's kitchen, a man was typing, very slowly. He had bright curly red hair. When I came in, he turned round. The first thing I noticed was his innocent expression. He looked as if he saw everything for the first time, like children do.

'Today, I had an awful feeling of grief in the Luxembourg Gardens,' I said.

The man did not say anything. He had huge pale-blue eyes, wide open. A black cane hung over his chair.

I knew it must be Patrick, Anthony's best friend, the American who had written a story about the old lady and the cat. He had been ill for a long time because of pollution from a paint factory outside San Francisco where he lived. The fumes from the paint had got into his lungs. He had sued the factory, and come over to Europe with the money. But the lawsuit had taken three years.

'What did you think of my story about the old lady and the cat?' he asked.

I said I thought it was too lavatorial.

'Maybe it is. I used to go to that café every day and write in my notebook. The old lady there didn't like me. Would you like some wine?'

He leaned over and took a bottle of Algerian wine out of his rucksack. It was the cheapest you could get, said to be made of chemicals instead of grapes.

When he leaned over, I saw how thin he was. I knew he had had a piece of his chest removed, so that now it was completely caved in. When he picked up the wine, his hand trembled.

I was hot, there was no place to sit; all the papers necessary to face offices, banks, the governments of countries, were in different pockets. I could not go into offices or banks with any appearance of calm. I could not pretend to follow their rules. I always seemed poorer than I was because I did not know how to control money. I could not control a house, a flat or even a room. I preferred living in other people's places, absorbing their atmospheres. They at least had a structure. They bought books, hung up pictures, made curtains, with conviction. They had records stacked in alphabetical order and some even had the latest type of record player.

When I inhabited a room, I filled it with books and newspapers. If I hung up pictures, it was as though I were copying other people.

I was sick of wearing jeans all the time, of running round the streets like a boy. It was frustrating to be a woman. You couldn't experience things in the same way. You always had to be careful. I couldn't go alone into bars in the Marais late at night, for instance. I couldn't talk to strange men, out of simple curiosity, without being picked up.

At the moment I didn't much like the company of other women, except for Simone. Women seemed to have no depth, no soul. It was difficult to explain. Also, their attitude to men fell between two extremes. Either a woman had one man she adored, on whom she depended completely so that she lost all character of her own, or she passed from one man to another, without recognizing the individuality of each of them. Women were often bland. Women were rarely generous in the same way men were generous. Or so I thought. Or was I turning into Alastair Crowley?

It was a few days after Claude's birthday party. I had decided to go to a film in the Latin Quarter, but suddenly I wanted to leave. It was as though someone were calling me. I started running down the rue Saint-Jacques. It was cold and raining. I felt I was the only person in the city. I crossed the river to the Île de la Cité and went into Notre-Dame. It was peaceful. I put in a franc for a candle and lit it, meaning it to be for Claude. An image of my brother flashed across my mind as I was in the church. Then I hurried back to the Marais. As I crossed the

175

second part of the Seine, I thought about death. It seemed close. I remembered how I had once said to Claude, '*Tu vas mourir.*' It was an odd thing to say.

Upstairs in the flat Anthony was drinking tea. We reminisced about the evening of Claude's birthday, and laughed. Then Anthony went out alone, to eat couscous.

I got into my sleeping-bag and went to sleep. I was woken by Claude. We were polite to each other. He came into my room and repacked his suitcase with the clothes he'd left in the flat, putting the case against my bedroom door. He said he was going back to Toulouse. I was aware that I was in the room alone with him.

'You were afraid when you woke up,' he said.

'I'm not nervous,' I replied.

I saw him looking at something I had left on the floor, something I'd written. It was about Philippe being my lover in Crete.

Claude asked me for Colette's watch, which I'd borrowed.

I said, 'I want to write her a note.'

For some reason, he looked displeased. I started to write the note, then gave up. I said I couldn't write informal French.

I asked him, 'Do you want the pineapple I gave you?'

He said he already had too much to carry. 'I'll see you when I come back to Paris.' Then he kissed me on each cheek. He said, 'Now you can go back to sleep.'

I went out with him on to the staircase. I said, 'Tell Colette I hope she's all right, and that I was wearing her watch.'

Then I heard him close the front door of the building.

For a moment I was sad, then I became stronger. I washed my hair and put on my skirt.

I went home that weekend on the hovercraft. I took a bus to the French coast. On the way we passed some of the grave-yards of those killed at the Somme. My grandfather, my mother's father, lay in one of those graveyards, but I didn't know which.

My father and mother were interested in my accounts of life in the Marais. My mother, already unstable, said she couldn't have stood that kind of bohemian life herself. My father asked whether Simone was pretty. Was she blonde or brunette? What was her voice like?

'I always have to hear a woman's voice before I decide whether or not I find her seductive,' said my father. He had been many times to Paris himself, and enjoyed it. He had been on jaunts there with one of our cousins on his mother's side – FR, a bachelor.

My mother and also my aunt (my father's sister) disapproved of FR. They said he was decadent and was a bad influence on my father. My mother said that after Paris had been occupied by the Germans, it had lost its soul.

I bumped into my old friend Rose at Victoria Station. She had gone back to her boyfriend Jake, and had just seen him off on a train. She told me they were engaged. She then confessed that she was pregnant. I had the feeling that she didn't want to get married, but couldn't admit it. I sensed that the whirlwind romance that she had had with her future husband, who, in his twenties, had already had two plays on Broadway, had lost its edge now that he had returned to Britain and they had decided to settle down. Nevertheless, Rose was the first of my school-friends to marry and have a baby. Although I did not want to get married myself, in emotional matters, it seemed, she was always one step ahead of me.

Before I returned to France, I visited my brother in London. He was still with his girlfriend, Sheila. As I took in their comforting domesticity – the green and white Chinese tea-pot, the rug from Afghanistan, Sheila's oatmeal-coloured cloak slung over a chair, a pair of her light-blue knickers on the radiator, my brother's favourite books (William Burroughs, Edgar Allan Poe, Ray Bradbury, even a new paperback called *Hindi: Self-taught*) – I felt envious and wondered whether I would ever have a partner myself, or even a successful love affair.

Perhaps I knew the answer already. My brother, whom I loved, and who was later to cause me so much sorrow, was my real soulmate, and I would never find another.

Harry

The first time I went to his flat in the Latin Quarter Harry was having a shower. His grinning wet face appeared from behind plastic curtains. He had smooth white cheeks and his eyes were a pale, cold blue. He was not at all embarrassed at being caught without any clothes on; he even seemed pleased.

In the room next door he had twin beds placed side by side. Above one bed was a map of Africa. On the wall was a map of the world and hundreds of bottle-tops stuck to a piece of card. On the bare floor was an old HMV record player, innumerable records that had been popular in London in the early sixties and piles and piles of newspapers, mostly from African countries. Harry was a journalist with a news agency and a specialist on Africa.

Harry took me on his motorbike to a French restaurant where we ate rich French food and drank a lot of wine. Over my rabbit, and Harry's steak, he revealed to me the personal lives of those we knew who lived in a commune in north London, where my friend Andrew was now living. (He had fled there from Bethnal Rouge.) This commune was run by a man whom Harry had nicknamed the former Lord Radley. The former Lord Radley's father owned a small stately home which was open to the public. His son had renounced these privileged origins. His heroes were Che Guevara, Castro and Chairman Mao.

Harry, who often visited London, said he had been 'having scenes with' Joanna, one of the girls in the commune. He described how they had had sex. He was coarse, I decided. As he talked, he leaned across the table as though he wanted to make love to me as well.

'Like all women, she thought it was her fault we weren't having a good time,' he said, wiping butter off his chin. 'She was getting sore, but she wouldn't admit it because she thought that if she did, it would be her fault I didn't come.'

I detested these kinds of confessions. They were supposed to show a liberated attitude to sex, but in fact were deadeningly clinical.

'Her father's got a big farm in South Africa,' Harry continued. 'They're rich. She's hung up about it. The other day her parents came to England. They said, "Why don't you get some nice clothes, instead of living in this mess here?" The next evening she slit her wrists and collapsed on the kitchen floor. Tried to do herself in.'

'Goodness.'

'I call it the Richmond Road Kitchen Floor Incident,' said Harry smugly. He obviously fancied himself as the psychiatrist of his friends. 'They think of me as a sane, healthy guy, who they can ask advice from about the commune,' he told me.

When we left the restaurant, Harry took me on the back of his motorbike to the news agency where he worked. He seemed proud of working there. I could not focus or concentrate on what he was saying. We looked at the typewriters tapping away. At one desk spools of tape were coming out of a machine.

'Suppose you missed an important bit of news, would you get the sack?' I asked.

'If Nixon had been assassinated and I missed it, yes, I'd get the sack,' said Harry. 'Now, do you want to try to write a story?'

Harry handed me a typed paragraph, about the visit of a black prime minister to a white official. The phrase which caught my imagination was 'hewers of wood and drawers of water'. The prime minister had told the white official that black people could no longer be defined as 'hewers of wood and drawers of water'. It was time for them to work to make their own countries economically self-sufficient, using their own resources. I had to paraphrase this.

'What you do here is rewrite what's already reported,' I said. 'It's completely secondhand. You get excited about these events and all you're doing is reflecting them.'

'Yes, that's right,' said Harry.

Another journalist, an American with an enormous head, came up to Harry. They discussed some reports from America in businesslike tones. The American was strange-looking, like a waxwork. None of the journalists, except for Harry, were animated. It was probably the sort of job that made one tired, bored and cynical. You got well paid, but at the end no one quite knew why. If you could manage words skilfully, you should really be writing original stories and articles, I thought, not doing this automatic job. But you would not be paid so much.

I watched Harry strut round the office, showing me the different machines. I could not take this professionalism seriously. It seemed a game where men showed off to each other.

'Is it OK if I leave for about half an hour?' said Harry to the American. He had decided to buy me a book on Africa.

Five minutes later we were speeding through Paris on the motorbike. I hoped he was not the sort of man who showed off to girls by riding dangerously. Sometimes we squeezed in between cars and I was afraid for my knees.

It began to rain. It was horrible. My behind was now wet from the bike seat. Harry parked at place Saint-Michel. The lit-up fountain was surrounded by young travellers from different countries, perhaps with nowhere to sleep. They were sitting underneath the fountain, eating stodgy food, the food I had also eaten when I had come alone to Paris two years before: crêpes, or Tunisian sandwiches – huge rolls stuffed with spicy vegetables and fat olives. For many of them it was probably first time in Paris.

Harry led me to a bookshop called Joie de Lire. He put one arm protectively across my back. In the shop he bought me a paperback on Africa. It cost fourteen francs. The author told how Africa was exploited by richer countries.

We stood outside, waiting for the rain to stop. A dark-faced boy, perhaps an Arab, with spots, not realizing I was with Harry, teased me and asked my name, and whether I was German.

'No, I'm English.'

'What is the cheapest way to get to London?' he said, playing the fool.

'Ask the travel agency.'

Harry watched us uncertainly from the other side of the door. I knew he thought me odd. He liked to be able to sum up the people he met.

The rain stopped and we got on the motorbike again.

'Do you know any bars in the Marais near where you're staying?' asked Harry.

'No, I don't,' I said. 'I dare say we could find one.'

We drove round the Marais in the pouring rain. The only bar that was open was filled with unshaven men.

'You don't want to go in there, do you?' said Harry. 'You don't want to be the only girl.' I thought perhaps he used this as an excuse, because *he* didn't want to go into the bar.

'I've been in Mick's Café in Fleet Street late at night,' I boasted. 'I was the only girl then. I was dressed up, in a velvet frock and a purple hat. Everyone stared at me.'

'Hm.' Harry went on driving round and round the same streets. We passed a huge red building that was lit up. Harry said he didn't know anything about architecture and didn't want to. Similarly, he had bragged earlier about only having read three novels in his life.

I was freezing. 'Maybe I'd better go home,' I said feebly.

'Come on,' said Harry, patting me on the knee. 'I'll take you to my office again.'

'How will I get home?'

'I'll give you the money for a taxi.'

When we were still on our way to the office, Harry began describing the personalities of his colleagues and giving thumbnail character sketches of them. The first person we saw, outside the large café opposite the agency, was an American woman who worked with him.

'That's the Yellow Hippo. She's marvellous,' he told me. 'She's an exile from her country, for political activity. She's got enormous hips.'

'Is that nice?' I asked.

'Well, I don't know.' Harry looked a bit confused. (I had narrow hips.)

'At least she didn't have to use forceps when she had a child,' I said.

Then we went into the bar. My hair, which, earlier that evening, had been soft and shining was now soaked. We sat down at a table with the American woman. She looked pleasant, I thought. She had long black hair and her teeth stuck out.

'Be careful on that motorbike,' she said to me. 'We once had an accident when I was on it and he just left me lying on the street. He was more concerned about the bike than about me.'

Later I went back to the Marais in a taxi. It was 2 a.m.

I woke with an awful cold. I had a clear vision of Claude's grey eyes and pale face. I went into the street wearing Claude's coat. I went through the Tuileries, getting caught up in a crowd of small children. The park already seemed like a park in winter, white and cold and bare.

I passed Cartier's window again, where the leopard brooch was still seated on its velvet cushion.

I carried on, past the Ritz Hotel. Outside the American Express office, where I collected my fifty pounds, an African was advertising a Volkswagen bus for sale.

By this time I was sweating, with fever. I walked all the way back to the Marais, along a street called the rue des Lombards. Here I came upon a demolition site, with gaunt buildings behind. They were the old buildings of Les Halles.

In the boulevard Sébastopol I was stopped by some French boys wanting to do a questionnaire on racism. I didn't like being on the street on my own for any longer feeling ill, so I said no. Instead, I bought *Le Monde* to read about the Arab–Israeli War, which had just begun. Perversely, it made me feel very excited.

Harry disapproved of my aimless life in the Marais, and of what I told him about Anthony and Patrick. He called them Los Negativos or Those Who Live Off Their Grandmothers'

Cheques in the Polly Magoo. (This was one of their favourite bars, on the rue Saint-Jacques.)

The second time I went to his flat Harry was more subdued, or perhaps it was simply that I was ready for him. He had washed his hair.

He offered me some fat white grapes, and read an account written by a friend of his, of the friend's father's death. The father had been a science professor in Scotland, and had died of a heart attack. His son, then twenty, was called away from his university in the south, but he arrived too late, just after his father had died. Nevertheless, he went upstairs and pulled away the sheet. White pads were over his father's eyes. His jaw was tied up with a cloth. The boy felt separate from his mother and sister, and superfluous to the occasion. He had imagined himself being efficient and arranging details like the funeral hymns, but in fact it was his sister who did it all.

After Harry had read this out, I felt more sympathetic towards him. He told me that his own father, who had died while *he* was at university, had been a sailor, a builder, a draughtsman and a journalist. He had also had an eccentric yearning for luxurious cars, and had kept a Rolls-Royce and a Daimler, unused, in the garage for three years. When he died, he had left enormous debts. He was not really a businessman, said Harry.

I thought of my own father, who had also been a sailor. Later, outside the Greek restaurant, when we got off the motorbike, I told Harry this. I said my father had been naval attaché in Madrid.

'How come my father was a draughtsman and your father was a diplomat?' said Harry.

'Because they were from a different class, of course,' I said.

I sat down at one of the tables. It was covered with a white cloth. After ordering hors d'œuvres, Harry began to talk about his girlfriends.

'There's this Russian woman I have incredible scenes with,' he said. 'But our heads are so far apart that we can only get on in bed. So there's no future for us. How many times have you been in love?'

I replied that I thought I had been in love three times. 'The first person I was in love with had exactly the same handwriting as you. Not that I'm in love with you,' I added. (I was thinking of Martin.) 'We went round America on Greyhound buses,' I continued. 'I was influenced by his mind.'

'My God!' said Harry. It was obvious that he had never been influenced by anybody's mind. 'When did you have it off with him?' he asked.

'Never,' I said.

Harry leaned across the table. 'What do you mean? Who wouldn't? You wouldn't? Or he wouldn't? Were you a virgin?'

'No,' I said. 'Anyway, he was too obsessed with the fact that I had more money than he had.'

'I never have those hang-ups,' said Harry emphatically.

'Good,' I said. We occupied ourselves with the hors d'œuvres, making sure that we had one of each.

In spite of my reservations, I found I was seeing Harry often. His life was narrow in some ways. He hardly ever went to bars, as Patrick and Anthony did, nor did he know many French people. Most of Harry's friends in Paris were English, and he frequently had visitors over from England for weekends. He thought, perhaps correctly, that his bachelor lifestyle, with his large salary, his Parisian garret inside a courtyard, his frequent trips to Africa and his many girlfriends, seemed romantic to those stuck in boring jobs in Britain.

One evening Harry invited me out with Jim, an old friend whom he had nicknamed the Stoat Keeper. The Stoat Keeper had come over for two days from London. He uttered wise words with a straight face, delivering them in a curiously lethargic voice. In a French restaurant with red tablecloths, where the waitress refused to serve us with three different courses, saying we all had to have the same food, the Stoat Keeper told us about his sister, who had been a doctor but had given it up to become a salesgirl in Marks and Spencer. After selling handbags behind the counter, she was promoted to management because she was more capable than anyone else. All the other women were jealous, he said.

After the meal we went to the Palette, a trendy café near the Beaux Arts art school near Harry's flat, and drank, in surroundings of fashionable posters and dark wood walls. As usual, Harry talked about the former Lord Radley's commune in London and criticized a man who lived there, saying he was the most selfish person he had ever met. Whenever he had a sandwich, and you asked him for a bit, he refused.

'I shouldn't like to be his chick,' said Harry.

'Would you like to be *my* chick?' asked the Stoat Keeper. He told me and Harry that we were both 'out on a limb'. It would be interesting to see what happened to each of us in later life.

The next night I went out again with Harry and some more of his English friends. All of them, except one, had been nicknamed long ago by Harry, and it was difficult to find out their real names. They, like the Stoat Keeper, had come over from London.

There was the Communist Millionairess, who taught at a comprehensive school in Kilburn, His Ultimate Weirdness and the Onion Man. There was also Harry's oldest friend, with whom he had been at university in the north of England, and who had recently moved to Paris. This man for some reason was known as Chugga.

I felt completely alienated from the group. I began to see them as resembling animals. The girl, with fat arms and stubby fingers, and a large bosom, reminded me of an alligator. She kept opening her mouth, drawing her lips back and showing a row of little sharp teeth. Her cheeks were rosy. She was probably without malice, but on that occasion she seemed unpleasantly tough and crude. After she had drunk two pints of beer and a whisky and ginger ale, she said she was going to 'go wee-wee'. Later in the evening, after she had drunk two more whiskies and ginger ales, she said she was 'going to piss'. Before she disappeared to the lavatory, passing photographs of famous

Americans in Harry's Bar, where we now were, her new lover, Chugga, grabbed her left breast, and said something about her 'tit'. Did he want to draw attention to the fact that he was her lover? I thought that when people needed to make these kinds of gestures and use terms like 'tit' and 'screw', it showed that, contrary to what they were trying to convey, they were not liberated, but self-conscious.

The Onion Man, who had fuzzy greasy hair, towards the end of the evening began to show an interest in me. He repeated several times that I had lovely soft eyes, and took my hand across the table and squeezed it. He did not let go. I allowed him to hold my hand, but felt there was no other contact between us. The Onion Man had very long eyelashes and kept blinking them at me in a way that was meant to be benign, but seemed to me insincere. He said he wanted me to come to his cottage in Dorset.

'But I'm not going back to England,' I said.

'You can't say that. You never know what may happen tomorrow,' he said.

He told me his wife was a chief editor at an important magazine. 'She has three secretaries.' Although he pretended to disparage this, I guessed he probably said it because he thought I would be more impressed by his own status if it was enhanced by his wife's job. He was a teacher at a school in Pinner. We talked about monogamy and then the man said he was bisexual. I said I had only once fallen in love with a woman, at the convent where I was educated.

'You must admit we have a certain "*rapport*",' said the Onion Man, pronouncing the word like 'wrapper'.

'Yes,' I said weakly. (The reason I felt we had *rapport* was because he was the only one of the three who had bothered to talk to me.)

'Would you like to come out tomorrow evening?' said the man.

I said yes without thinking.

Meanwhile Chugga bit me in the shoulder and rolled his eyes. He was very stoned. Earlier in the evening I had thought

Chugga was a mild, gentle character. Now I saw his supposed gentleness as weakness. His animation was probably only due to his smoking Afghan hash each time before he went out. His eyes were unnaturally bright and his hair was newly washed. He was making love to the Communist Millionairess, Harry whispered, while her other lover, over with her from England for the weekend, slept on the floor in the next room, beside the Colombian girl who was Chugga's lodger. The Colombian girl was known by Harry as the Gerbil and was not with us. Nor was the Communist Millionairess' other boyfriend.

In the Marais the following morning the full horror of the English people struck me. Harry himself reminded me of a piece of white sausage meat. The Onion Man, with his long eyelashes and phoney gentleness, was, in retrospect, even more repulsive. The girl who was a millionairess seemed even more like an alligator, with her sharp little teeth. Why hadn't I gone home straight after our Afghan meal instead of going on with them to a bar? I thought. Also, I was sick of Harry boasting about Africa and his old girlfriends.

Simone and Anthony, with their idea of 'the artist' as someone different and special, seemed delicate and unworldly in comparison. Simone, although she worked nine to five, thought that to have a regular job ('*métro, boulot, dodo*') was 'death to a creative spirit'.

I had read her diary one day when she had left it in the kitchen. In it she had described Anthony as 'a tortured poet'. I had seen a poem he had written and it wasn't that good. He was definitely tortured, though. He was constantly hiding from the blows of life, but to other people the experiences he found so painful wouldn't have been blows at all.

I knew that even these excursions into bars really were, for him, like going into battle. The rest of the time he spent asleep, or sitting in the kitchen with a rug over his knees, reading. When he woke up, usually around five in the afternoon, he would lie in bed for an hour or two, going over in his head what had happened to him the day before. 'The only job I could do would be something like gardening, where I could still think my own thoughts,' he told me.

We were often alone together in the kitchen, usually when he first came out of his bedroom in the early evening. If he wasn't going out to eat, he would stand by the stove wearing a fake fur coat, trousers tucked into his socks like a cyclist, and heat up a tin of lentils and sausages. I couldn't resist flirting a bit with him. I liked him, and I found his uncompromising purity, and his thin, gaunt body, attractive. I told myself, however, that he was too frail and weak to be my lover. Anyway, he was Simone's.

One evening, when Simone came in from work late – Anthony was out – she seized a piece of crispbread, and we started talking about our families. I described how, when I had felt vulnerable during a bout of glandular fever, I had seemed to enter my mother's mind. I had been convalescing at my grandmother's and my mother had driven over to visit me. I guessed that my mother was brooding about my brother Jonathan. I was sure she thought, how can they laugh and be happy here, when the house is full of ghosts?

Simone said she had had a similar experience, when her father was very ill. He had anorexia. In the middle of the night, she recalled, he had walked, painfully slowly, to the fridge and eaten a spoonful of yoghurt. She said she had had a cold feeling, an awful coldness, and knew that this was what her father was feeling all the time.

When I woke up next morning, there was sun coming into the room. I was perfectly happy. I went into the kitchen, where the sun was coming through the window on to the stove and the blue paint that was the kitchen walls. Simone came in. She started to cry, and made lunges towards the window, as if she were trying to reach for the sun. She was shaking all over. She tried to make some coffee, but her hands were trembling so much she couldn't do it. She clutched at her stomach with one hand, and her face streamed with tears. I stood at the stove, perfectly calm. I reached for a filter and put some coffee into it.

I wanted to hug Simone to comfort her, but I was too awkward.

Instead, I got a broom and swept out my room. I put Anthony's cat posters into a drawer, and all Colette's stuff, including her laxatives, and the journals of Anaïs Nin, on one shelf. I was nervous after Simone's fit. I was torn between detaching myself from it, as a form of self-protection, or, in sympathy, submerging myself in the terror that Simone must have felt.

Simone drank about three bottles of wine every night. Patrick assured me that she did it because she suffered from dreadful insomnia. A few nights before her fit, when Patrick and I had been talking on the mattress in my little room, Simone had sobbed for hours in the kitchen, and eaten all the food, though there wasn't very much anyway.

'I thought at first it was the cooing of pigeons,' said Patrick the next day.

'But she doesn't have to cry like that,' I said. I meant that Simone should have more self-control.

'She's had insomnia for two years,' said Patrick. 'Drinking wine's the only way she can get to sleep.'

I had met Patrick by chance that day in the avenue de l'Opéra. I had the sensation that I was flying. We went into a café and he had three beers, and I had a vichy menthe. We stayed there for two and a half hours. Patrick asked, 'Why do you always have a faraway look?' I said I didn't know.

Harry, as my father had been, continued to be intrigued by my stories of life in the Marais, but he had not yet met Los Negativos.

One evening, when I was on the back of his motorbike outside the Drugstore Saint-Germain, I pointed out Anthony, walking alone down a side street. Harry remarked on his long bony nose and the way he had the collar of his coat pulled up round his neck, like a monk's cowl. After that he called Anthony the Bird Monk.

I felt a bit disloyal. I was fond of Anthony. Also, I was discomfited at the thought of my two worlds meeting. Harry was dominating. I did not want him knowing about every area of my life.

I had also begun to talk to Anthony and Patrick about Harry. They were disparaging, as they often were of anything English. One evening Anthony demonstrated how a French person would push open the exit doors of the metro station – with his body – and how an English person would do it – with his hands, at a distance. Anthony and Patrick assumed that Harry, whom they dubbed the English Journalist, would fit their corny idea of an Englishman. I had told them he was tough and ambitious and they said they despised these qualities.

One day at 4 p.m. I found Anthony standing at the kitchen window. Rain was pouring off the black roofs.

He said, 'This is the day I had prepared to go for a walk. I'd been thinking about it for weeks.'

'Do you think of yourself as a filter, or do you think of yourself as in control, when you're writing?' I asked.

'I think of myself as out of control the whole time,' Anthony replied.

I had an image of him being dominated all the time by Life, in the form of a powerful black snake. I thought that probably I too could be in control, like Harry, if I wanted, but that I still wanted unexpected things to happen.

Anthony and Patrick's attitude to drinking in the Latin Quarter bars both mystified and annoyed me. Setting off with them one evening, I heard Anthony nervously asking Patrick, 'Where do you go? Do you go to the Saint-Severin?' as though which bar one went to revealed one's character.

The two men would often come home drunk at five in the morning, and then tell bar stories over and over again, about throwing glasses across the room, or Patrick being accosted by a Guadeloupian whore, or Anthony arguing with an American poet, as though they had just been performing the most dangerous feats on a battlefield.

I liked Patrick better now, although I still wasn't sure if we were going to have a sexual relationship.

Instinctively I felt Patrick was worth more than Harry, but why did I think that? Maybe I could only have awful men as lovers, or men I thought were awful. Perhaps I found crude, tough men more masculine, or maybe I wanted to think that the men that I was attracted to were like that. At any rate, I wanted to put them to the test. Perhaps some kind of fight, or opposition, was necessary to me. Patrick was too compliant.

One night, in the flat, I told Patrick some stories about me and Carla in Greece. He replied with anecdotes about various girls he'd met in bars. He even had a rendezvous with a Persian girl that evening, at midnight. When I went to bed later, I wished I had not gone on my own. Suddenly sex seemed very easy. (Of course it was, but afterwards? It was *being* with the other person which wasn't easy.)

In the middle of the night, after Patrick had left, I heard Anthony switch off the light and go to the bedroom. I thought stupidly, he and Simone must be making love. How lucky they are.

Then, after about half an hour, Simone went into the kitchen. I could hear her sobbing. She sounded distraught. After a while I divorced myself from her grief. I thought perhaps she was crying because she could not make love after an operation she had had in the summer. On the other hand, she might have been weeping for some other reason, such as her father being ill. I thought about how I had learned to detach myself from situations. I should have rushed in there and made her a cup of tea.

At dawn I heard Simone making a moaning sound in the bathroom.

In the morning I found a note where the muesli packet had been, saying she had eaten everything in the flat and now she had an 'obligation' to buy more. I thought it was a rather puritan note, considering I was staying in her flat free. I went to the local shop and bought honey, muesli, milk and cheese.

Simone had left her diary in the kitchen again. Perhaps she wanted me to read it. Or maybe she had left it there because she was too confused to remember where it was. This time I read only one paragraph, about Anthony being vulnerable. (I assumed it was Anthony.) I felt nervous reading it, since Simone was still next door in her bedroom.

It was All Souls' Day. I woke up feeling very depressed. I thought it was probably because I had not had sex for a long time. Also, I had been freezing cold all night. The eiderdown had slipped off, but I had been too sleepy to pull it on again. Throughout the night I had been vaguely aware of Anthony typing next door.

In the kitchen there were sunflower seeds all over the floor, and empty milk bottles. The sink was filled with saucepans containing tomato sauce and water. I did not want to wake up. My day was already polluted by Simone's depression. What did she want of me? Some kind of strength or advice. But she was pulling me under.

In the afternoon Patrick was there again, typing out a story. I did not know whether I wanted to go to bed with him or not. While he was typing, I sat on the sofa sewing a button on Claude's coat, which was now mine. Once Patrick turned round to see if I was still there. I got the impression that he was afraid of me. He seemed far kinder than I was.

Anthony had told us he was going out to eat couscous, but then he didn't go. He sat on a chair, between me and Patrick. With his body he was telling me he didn't want Patrick to make love to me.

Later I chatted to Anthony, wearing the Dr Dentons yellow pyjamas that Carla had left for me when she went to Los Angeles. I had wrapped myself in an eiderdown. Anthony advised me to read *Maurice*, a homosexual novel by E. M. Forster.

The next evening Simone was again in tears. She started to tell me she was in love with someone else, which I had already suspected from reading her diary again. She seemed completely passive and helpless, open to terror and confusion, her own and other people's.

Before I went to bed, I thought defiantly, it's absurd to refrain from going to bed with someone because I think they might despise me. I shall make love with whomever I like.

I dreamed I went back to a seaside village which, in my dream, represented the village in Crete. Philippe was there, but he ignored me. I knew that this was because I had been so free before.

The next morning I remembered another dream I had had in the night. I was sitting in a car with a fortune-teller, only she was telling my fortune from my knee, not my hand. She had brown wrinkled skin. She told me that I had missed a love further back, and that I had gone wrong. I realized that this was the thing I was afraid of, of missing love. Women's romance, perhaps.

My relationship with Patrick had changed. It was now late November and it was cold. One evening I went out with Anthony and Patrick to have couscous. Patrick looked tense. His eyes seemed very blue in his chalk-white face. He was wearing a blue denim shirt with the initials BF on the lapels. 'Big Fucker,' he said, pointing to it. He was shy of me, and I of him. Having made a small advance to him one evening in a bar, I was too embarrassed to follow it up.

We went to a Moroccan café with plain yellow walls and a pinball machine. No one was eating. A few Algerian men were standing up at the bar. The waiters there were friendly. The three of us sat down and asked for chicken couscous. Patrick was trembling. He reached inside his jacket and took out a pill. He was an epileptic.

A woman came in as we had almost finished our meal. Patrick was eating up the skin of the chicken, from which he had torn the flesh. She came and touched Patrick on the shoulder. 'You are American, sir?' She was tiny, with shining eyes. She sat down at the table behind us. 'I am just an old Jew,' she said. Then she began to talk about Toronto, where she had stayed in a hotel that was too expensive for her. 'I was so hungry,' she moaned.

'I could not eat for three days. I had no money. North Gate. I hate Toronto.'

None of us knew whether she was drunk or not. She went on talking about Toronto, while she ate couscous and a cutlet, which she had on a side plate. The waiter appeared to know her.

'But if the hotel was too expensive, why didn't you find a cheaper one?' I said.

The woman came and sat next to Patrick, leaving the rest of her food. I reached behind her and put it on our table. It was vegetables in hot grease. Patrick and I began to eat it.

The woman told us she was the daughter of Modigliani. She said that Canadian television had invited her to go to Toronto. That was why she had gone there. They wanted to interview her about her father. 'And do you know the one question they asked me? "Who was your father's last mistress?" I replied, "My mother, of course."'

She turned to Patrick, as if expecting applause. She asked us a question about culture.

Patrick began playing the fool. 'Shakespeare, who was Shakespeare? What's a playwright?'

Anthony responded seriously to her and talked about the painter Pollock. Patrick pretended that he was a painter, who lived off his friends.

'What kind of painting?' asked Modigliani's daughter.

'I draw three lines, and I try to make them not touch,' said Patrick, demonstrating with his hands stuck out in front of him. He seemed to be avoiding any real contact with the woman.

Anthony's face looked very white under the electric light. Before Modigliani's daughter came in, he had told me and Patrick a story about one Christmas Eve, when a man had 'humped' another girl in front of his own wife.

When the meal was over, Modigliani's daughter invited us back to a flat near by. She put on a revolutionary record. The words went something like this: 'I have pants, the workers have no pants.' She did a little dance for us. Then we left.

*

194

Harry had made me feel guilty for not working, so I decided to go and ask for some editorial work at the *Herald Tribune*. First I drank coffee at Simone's, and read some articles in *Le Monde*, to prepare myself. Then Simone came in from outside, wearing a coat which made her look like a blue Mother Christmas. She had bought it in a flea market. It was navy, and had a hood and a fur collar. She sat on the sofa reading a letter. Her face got red, and she started to weep.

I went on reading the articles.

Then I took the metro to George V. I got out in a curiously impersonal area, not smart, as I had expected. It was still the lunch hour so I walked up a few streets, and went into a café and ordered a hot chocolate. I was sitting in a conspicuous place in the middle of the room, reading the *Herald Tribune*. There was a piece about an Israeli general, part of the news about the Arab–Israeli War.

I walked back up the street towards the *Herald Tribune* offices. I looked at the list near the door. Editor, managing editor, publicity. I thought editor, or managing editor, was the right one. The liftman helped me. I walked up one floor, saw a man in a suit come out with a cross expression, then I walked down and back into the street. I didn't feel like going in. I pretended to myself it was because I had nothing to offer, and perhaps I hadn't. I thought the liftman must think I was a fool. I was sweating and felt very bad-tempered.

Patrick said, 'Well, are you coming?'

We were back in Simone's flat. He had been talking to a French girl's mother on the telephone.

Earlier we had discussed jealousy. I had said, 'If I'm jealous, it means I feel lust for someone. People I've just been fond of I've never been jealous of.' (I wasn't sure if this was strictly true.)

I began to do my washing, at the kitchen sink, while Patrick sat waiting for the French girl to ring up. Even by nine o'clock she hadn't rung. By that time I was angry. I wrung out my washing violently. Then I sat at the kitchen table, under the lamp, reading *Le Monde*.

Patrick rose. He said again, 'Well, are you coming?'

'I don't know,' I said. I wanted to be asked.

'Are you hungry?' said Patrick.

'Yes.'

'You'd better come, then.'

I put on my red scarf and coat, and ran downstairs, with relief. Patrick followed me slowly as he was lame. We began our walk through the streets. For some reason, my eyes kept filling with tears. I thought perhaps it was because I had begun to love Patrick. I hid my face by looking in shop windows. Then we crossed the Seine. I felt very small beside Patrick, who was so tall.

'I'm going to take you to a couscous place in the rue de Bièvre,' he said.

When we entered the restaurant, everyone was immobile, except for a half-grown Alsatian puppy. A broad woman, with hair tucked behind her ears, stood against the counter, arms akimbo. Her calves were fat. She was like a statue that had been put there, a statue which did not fit in with the rest of the décor. Everyone was looking at Patrick. Perhaps this was because he took so long to sit down. Also, he was conspicuous. He was very tall and white-faced and ill, and he had haunted large eyes, very blue.

Patrick ordered couscous bœuf for both of us and some red wine. Then he began to talk about his financial situation. Usually his mother sent him money from California, but this time she had not sent any.

'I don't like asking her for money,' said Patrick. 'Anyway, this time I don't think she has any. All her relatives have just died.'

I wondered if Patrick meant, 'I want you to pay for the meal.'

'Do you think you're devious?' I said, meaning, 'Why don't you ask me to pay for the meal?'

'Maybe,' said Patrick.

'It's a drag, living like that,' I said. 'Always waiting for money.'

Suddenly I adopted the pose of a rich woman. I became very conscious of my eye make-up. Perhaps for a moment I looked capable and hard, though I was not like that.

'Why do you visit your grandmother?' Patrick asked.

'Why do you think I visit her?' I asked.

'Is she senile?' asked Patrick.

Suddenly my face softened. 'She's very courageous,' I said. 'She's not senile at all.'

Then Patrick began to talk about *his* grandmother, whom he disliked. 'When I was a little boy,' he said, 'she took me aside, and told me "I wish you'd remain like you are now, but you won't, you'll grow up." I hated her.'

'Do you think Simone's like a child?' I asked.

'Well, the other day, she came in with that honey,' said Patrick, and laughed.

Simone had bought a jar of honey in a paper jar, which cost eighteen francs. She had rhapsodized about the pattern on the side of the jar, which was a mass-produced picture of alpine flowers under a blue sky.

'I'm not an adult because people have always looked after me,' said Patrick. 'Perhaps because I was ill.'

'But I met someone who was on his back with a spinal injury for two years,' I said, 'and it made him more adult and serious. It's a question of temperament.'

'Being adult is also a question of accepting work,' said Patrick. 'I don't accept that you have to work.'

'I think that being adult is accepting that life is unpleasant,' I said. 'Who wants to do that?'

Patrick was now piling couscous on to both our plates. The statuesque woman with hair tucked behind her ears had disappeared.

I could feel his leg pressing mine under the table. I wanted to make love with him. His wrists were covered with long soft greyish hairs. I knew, from seeing him one day in the bathroom, that his chest was cream white, without any hairs, and that only half of it remained.

Patrick reminisced about his grandfather, who had had a plantation in Tennessee. Then I talked about Crete and how I had stolen Philippe's clothes on the beach in Mátala.

There was a map of Algeria on the wall. I said, 'What am I doing here in Paris, when there's so much to see everywhere else?' Suddenly I wanted to be in a hot place, where there was sun and dust on the streets, an Arab country, perhaps, where I had never been.

Patrick went and telephoned the French girl again. I thought we would make love that night, but after the meal, after he returned from telephoning, our contact was broken.

He asked, 'Where are you going now?'

I said, 'Back to the flat, I suppose.'

I thought he might still ask me to go home with him. I felt insulted and vulnerable. I walked with him along the boulevard Saint-Germain, looking into the cafés. There were a few girls sitting on their own, studying. I wanted Patrick to put his arm round me, but he didn't.

As we turned into the rue Saint-Jacques, he said he was going up the hill, then decided to take the metro instead. He looked completely vague and lost.

He said, 'See you' and I walked back to the flat, feeling terrible lust and anger all night, anger at his not understanding.

Harry woke me up by telephoning early the next morning. He told me to come round and have lunch.

At 12.30 I walked to his flat. There was a bright-blue sky. Harry's curtains were closed. All his files about Africa were on his bed. He showed me an article he had had in an English newspaper the day before, about Mugabe.

He wanted me to say his article was good, but I wouldn't. I said, 'Well, all articles in a daily paper are similar. There isn't much room to say anything.'

Then Harry's friend the Onion Man arrived. He was over again from England. We all went and had lunch. The two men argued all the way through. They both wanted to be the centre of the stage. I had *coquille Saint-Jacques*, in a brown sauce. The Onion Man said he wanted to take me out the next night. After the three of us left the restaurant, Harry took me alone to a café, where he spent two hours trying to persuade me that the Onion Man was ambitious, unintelligent and insecure.

I said, 'You took me to this café to shit on your friend.'

Then I walked home. Patrick was asleep on the sofa in the kitchen. He was so thin that Anthony's coat covered him completely. It seemed as if there were no body underneath.

It was my birthday. I was so drunk that I could hardly put my glass down. There was white around me. There was singing in my ears. The Englishman, the Onion Man, the man with the shiny nose who was trying to impress, had given me as a last drink a glass of wine called a Rosebud, named after the bar we were in. If the other waiter, Gil, had been there, the Onion Man explained, Gil would have made it a proper drink, with more flavour and plenty of herbs. But Gil was on holiday.

When my escort (not a good description, but what else was he?) went to the bathroom, a Greek, who said he was a painter, came up to me. His sunken eyes looked part of the skin on his face, sketched there by accident. He was talking about astronomy and the sun. He said there were holes in the sun. I could only think of sex. I wanted to put my arms round the Onion Man, who had now come back and was standing beside the Greek. I wanted to fuck. The world of politics this man was talking about was completely irrelevant. Behind the face of the Greek, in the eyes, was something animal. I saw my own face in the mirror of the bar. I had wanted to put my arms round Patrick's head the other evening and say, 'I want to make love with you.' But I had been too inhibited. Surely all these pretences were absurd? We were animals after all. There was no point in talking. Talking was just repeating the words in *Le Monde*. It was nothing, nothing, nothing.

When I got back to the flat at 2 a.m., there was a strange

young man in the kitchen asleep. I took off my clothes and got into my sleeping-bag. The whole room was rocking like a boat. I thought I might be sick.

Harry had invited me to come with him to the Gerbil's birthday party. I arrived at his flat to find him absent. He had left a note on his door, saying he would be back later, and that the key was under the mat. I went in and sat as usual among all the files about Africa. I wondered whether to look through his mail, but as he seemed to lack much sense of secrecy, it would probably be no fun.

Soon Harry returned and prepared himself for a shower. He took off his shoes and socks in front of me. His feet were dirty.

'How often do you change your socks?' I asked.

'Once a week,' said Harry.

'No wonder men's feet smell so much,' I said, thinking of my father's bedroom.

'Nonsense,' said Harry. 'I may put on clean socks for the Gerbil's party, then put these old ones on again tomorrow,' he added.

He went into the kitchen, then walked back into the bedroom with a towel in front of his penis, but stood so that I could see his behind. It was not at all the sort of behind I was used to in men, being rather plump and hairy. As I had just been talking to Patrick, I found it difficult to establish immediate rapport with Harry.

'I am being pulled in two directions,' I said.

'Come in here and talk to me,' shouted Harry, now in his shower in the kitchen. 'I can't hear.'

I declined this obvious invitation. I sat on Harry's bed, looking vaguely at his books. Most of them were on Africa. I thought that in some ways he was using the continent to make himself important and interesting. He was always drawing attention to African countries, I noticed, when he felt insecure. I remembered how, in the Balkans restaurant in the Latin Quarter, he had started drawing maps of Rhodesia on the tablecloth because he was worried by something critical that I had said. Once he had shown me photographs of Sierra Leone. Among beautiful views of mountains and blue skies there was a picture of four black boys, standing in rags and grinning. So far, I had not discovered how earnest Harry was about helping to overthrow the corrupt governments in Africa. He was certainly anxious to establish himself as a member of a left-wing élite. He was always accusing others of being boring, emphasizing that he wanted nothing to do with 'boring' people. I thought this meant that he was afraid of being boring himself.

'I haven't bought a present for the Gerbil,' I said when Harry came out of the shower, grinning and twinkling his light-blue eyes. He succeeded sometimes in looking impish, despite his burly physique.

'Well, nor have I,' said Harry. 'We'll buy her some wine.'

The Gerbil, Chugga's flatmate, was small and serious, and her life was dull, though it was difficult to say why. She wanted to be with 'interesting' people, she said, and she thought Harry was one of these.

'Gerbil's been round here a lot recently,' said Harry. 'She comes round and sits on my knee. She likes me. I told her, "It wouldn't solve your problems if you sleep with me, you know, Claudia."'

'Well, I'd probably like her if I hadn't heard you and Chugga criticizing her all the time,' I said.

A few moments later we were whizzing along the boulevard Saint-Germain on Harry's motorbike. We stopped to buy some wine. My legs were cold because I was wearing a long dress and I had to pull it up to avoid it getting caught in the bike wheels. Being on the motorbike still made me nervous. Cars swung out of side roads without seeing us. If the road looked empty, Harry would accelerate. Neither of us wore crash helmets.

The Gerbil's party was on the other side of Montparnasse. It was being given in the flat of one of her girlfriends, Diane, who was French. According to Harry, Diane, as well as the Gerbil, liked him.

'We'll leave the party towards the end and go out drinking,' Harry told me.

As we tore along the empty road, I had the illusion that I was riding behind a demon. I thought of a ballad about a girl who had been tricked by a demon lover. Perhaps I would be tricked by Harry in the same way. He made me feel limp and weak, because he was assertive. My thighs, naked because I was wearing socks instead of tights, clung to his behind. I fantasized that I was under his power.

The flat was sumptuous compared with most places I had been to in Paris. There were several fancy chairs and proper beds with bedheads, and a fitted carpet. The Gerbil was wearing black tight trousers and a yellow shirt. She was already drunk, and this seemed to change her completely. Usually she was sober and serious. Tonight she was wild. Diane, her friend, was more sensible. They were expecting ten people to the party, but no one else had turned up. Diane had cooked delicious food. The first course was sauerkraut and sausage. Harry and I sat together on the sofa, opposite the two girls. Diane sat on the floor, a wary expression on her face. Perhaps this was because she felt she must protect her friend from Harry, despite liking him herself.

Certainly, the Gerbil did seem unhinged. Halfway through the meal she shouted, 'I love you!' at Harry. She ran up and kissed him on the mouth. He put his arms round her as if he were a bear and rubbed her up and down. He made faces at me so that she could not see. I thought this was cruel. Diane continued sitting in a demure pose on the floor.

When the sausages and sauerkraut were finished, Diane fetched cheese. One of the cheeses was like a cake. It was white, and it was covered with dried grapes and raisins. I ate as much of this as I could, without appearing greedy.

'I'm going to ring up Tim and ask if he'll come here after work,' Harry said.

He went into the hallway. Tim, who also worked at the agency, came from Scotland but had lived most of his life abroad. Unlike the other foreign journalists, he lived not in Paris, but in a small village in the middle of France. He was going to marry a French girl from this village. He had known her since she was fourteen. Harry said that Tim liked girls like that because they were 'no threat'. Tim was a gentle character, and I thought there was no reason why he shouldn't marry a submissive girl, if he loved her. Harry, it seemed, was intolerant of anybody who wasn't like he was.

He came back from telephoning. 'Tim may come later,' he said. 'We'll have to go to Harry's Bar,' he said to Diane and the Gerbil. 'We've told some American girls to go there.'

Neither the Gerbil nor Diane wanted to go to Harry's Bar. They wanted to go to a Latin American discotheque called L'Escale. Harry said he refused to pay twenty francs entry into a discotheque, and then twenty francs for a drink once you got in. This was not because he was mean, he explained – he was always lending his friends money – but because it was against his principles to be ripped off by discotheques.

I regretted having asked the American girls to meet us at Harry's Bar. I had thought the party would be in Chugga's flat near Harry's Bar, not down here beyond Montparnasse.

The girls tried to persuade Harry to take them to L'Escale. Instead, he went into the hall and used the telephone once more to ring up Harry's Bar and ask them to find the American girls.

The Gerbil and Diane were fed up. They asked, as if I were responsible for Harry, 'What is he doing?'

I went into the hall and stood beside Harry. He immediately began to rub his hands up and down my behind and then over my right hip bone.

'That's erotic,' I said.

'Joanna the South African used to like that,' he said. 'Let's have a fuck tonight,' he continued. 'I like sophisticated girls like you and Joanna, not those two in there.'

Inside the main room Diane was clearing up the remains of

the food. She looked serious. The Gerbil looked unhappy. This might have been because she thought there was something going on between Harry and me.

'Well, let's go to Harry's Bar,' said Harry.

The Gerbil said she wanted to go home to bed, and would I take a taxi with her to her flat? I did not understand why, unless it was to stop me going with Harry on the motorbike.

Harry asked Diane to go on the motorbike with him, perhaps out of politeness, or to make me jealous.

In the taxi the Gerbil seemed drunk and despondent. She was a small girl with a mournful face, and hooded eyelids. She kept asking me if Harry's Bar was near her flat.

'Yes,' I said crossly.

I got out at Harry's Bar and left her to go home in the taxi. Harry and Diane were already sitting at the bar drinking beer out of fawn mugs. Now that Diane was with Harry she had become more cheerful.

Harry invited us to his office as the American girls had not turned up. In the office Harry dominated the conversation by shouting at everyone who came in and yelling out any personal details he knew about them. The one I liked best was Tim, whom Harry had telephoned earlier. He had soft pale hair, blue eyes and a mild expression. Harry explained that the greatest tragedy of Tim's life was that he had left the only copy of a play he had written in a train.

'I'm very sorry,' I said to Tim.

Tim smiled. He told me he lived in the country near Clermont-Ferrand and came to Paris only three days a week. 'I hate big cities,' he said. Then he explained how the women in the south were less aggressive than the women in Paris. (Some people would have described them as less liberated.) 'If you're about to light a cigarette, they step forward and light it for you,' he said.

'And do you like that?' I asked.

'Very much,' he replied. For a moment I thought that it was possible for there always to be women like that, who were gentle and submissive, and pleasing to the eye. Rose, who had been to Moscow, had said the 'liberated' women there were like elephants, all dressed in baggy trousers and doing manual work. However, passive women often got badly treated.

I was deliberating about Harry and Patrick. I had no idea which one to choose, or if, indeed, any choice was necessary. Sometimes it seemed that they were choosing me.

I tried to see them objectively. Patrick, the American, I met most days in Anthony and Simone's kitchen; Harry, the Englishman, I was with in his own apartment. (Patrick had only a tiny room, in Montparnasse.)

I thought more about the two men and compared them. Harry was self-supporting and paid for my meals in expensive restaurants. He took me roaring through the streets on the back of his motorbike. With few clothes on, he looked like a wild beast, a gorilla. Some part of my nature admired this. The attraction of Harry was that he attacked life with spirit and enthusiasm. He could take charge of situations. He was the boss of incoming news at the agency, for instance. Other men obeyed him. If he went to a restaurant with a group, he took it upon himself to order what everybody wanted.

Patrick was the opposite. He waited to see what others would do. He was a passenger, a voyeur. He was like a child. He had spent some part of his life being ill with asthma, and so had got used to people looking after him. He was always being approached in restaurants and cafés, often by strangers he didn't want to speak to. He saw life from a bizarre angle. He wrote stories which were full of the words 'shit', 'fuck' and 'vomit', and about characters who seemed grotesque, who did grotesque things.

He took me to small couscous restaurants, where you could eat meat and vegetables swimming in grease for six francs. When we walked together through the streets of Paris, I had to slow down to match his pace. I had promised to buy him a new cane when I went back to England.

I rang up Harry late one evening at his office. He asked,

'Have you fucked Patrick? Go on, I know you have. What was it like to fuck a man with a caved-in chest? You can put that in a novel.'

I felt guilty and sad, as if, by listening to Harry talk in this way, I had betrayed Patrick. I thought also that Harry knew the worst parts of my character, which Patrick didn't want to admit to, perhaps because he was afraid of them. As we were getting on to the metro near Simone's flat early that day, Patrick had insisted that I was 'passive'. Maybe he wanted me to be like he was.

I wrote a letter to Rose in London, asking her which man she thought sounded more promising.

When I went round to Harry's the next time, we had the same conversations as we usually had, with him doing nearly all the talking. The subjects were: his old girlfriends, the former Lord Radley's commune, boring people and the distaste Harry had for those who 'attached false value' to novels, which Harry never read.

'He's very insular, really, isn't he?' I had said to his friend Chugga a few days before.

'Yes, he is,' Chugga had replied.

Harry's girlfriends were of different nationalities. He showed me photographs of them and described, sometimes, where they had made love. The ugliest, according to him, was New Zealand Vick and the prettiest was Miss Very Nice Nina.

It occurred to me that, with his weird nicknames for people, his attitude to women, his rough kind-heartedness, his uninhibitedness and the way he yelled orders, Harry was, in many ways, like my father.

Soon after that I finally made love with Harry for the first time. It was on a Sunday afternoon. It was winter. Nothing was happening in the flat in the Marais and my room was very cold. I decided to go out to the drugstore in Saint-Germain and buy some English Sunday papers. I had a cold, and my nose kept running. Outside the sky was clear blue. It was beautiful winter weather. Strolling along beside the Seine, I could not imagine why I had ever been unhappy in Paris.

After buying the papers, I walked to Harry's flat. As I entered the courtyard, I had a sense of peace. I realized that Harry made me feel secure, perhaps because he was so predictable. When I had first met him over two months earlier, I had not thought he was predictable at all.

Harry had been asleep when I rang the bell. He suggested that I get into bed with him, so I said yes. I could hardly see in the dark to fold my clothes. It was like holding on to a rock, or a bear. He had hair on his shoulders. I did not feel so much excited as safe. At first I was miles away from him. I thought of Patrick and at one moment I imagined Anthony's frail white limbs around me.

Afterwards we lay and talked, vaguely, or rather he did, about his girlfriends. I felt then that he could never strike anything deep in me. His openness was all very well, but surely something was lacking? He described Vi, yet another former girlfriend, a 'small-town girl', he said, who wore tartan trousers. They had met in Canada.

He said, 'For people like that, I'm refreshing. They've never met anyone before who'll talk to them openly, without any bullshit. It takes them off guard.'

The second time we made love it was better. Afterwards he looked magnificent, very young, as if he had been reborn. I said, 'You look handsome.'

He said, 'You look nice too, all soft and gentle.'

Then I lay back on his bed, on his sheepskin rug, staring at the posters on the ceiling. One was of a village in Benin. There was also an oval enamel notice which read 'This is Harry's pad.' Apparently when Joanna, his South African girlfriend from London, had seen this on a visit to Paris recently, she had said, 'I suppose your new girlfriend with the odd voice gave you that.'

'I thought it was petty of her,' Harry told me. 'She even purposely got your name wrong. I don't like neurotic girls,' he added.

*

Rose replied at once in answer to my question about the two men.

Patrick, she wrote, sounded, from my description, 'tied to his mother by a moneyed umbilical cord'. She was sure I would soon get tired of living at such a slow pace. She thought Harry sounded a better choice because he was a challenge. Perhaps thinking of her own early days with Jake, she emphasized the thrill of 'racing one's companion down a grassy slope and arriving breathless in a heap at the end'.

The next day I told Harry I could not go on staying in the flat in the Marais indefinitely – I had relied on Anthony and Simone's hospitality for too long – so he suggested that I move in with him.

I packed my bags and got a taxi in the rue de Rivoli. When I gave Harry's address, the driver said, 'Oh, you're going to the jungle. Well, it depends on what kind of girl you are. If you want to experience life, much better go to the jungle.'

'Yes, I like the jungle,' I replied.

Harry's light was on, and he was working at his desk. He was wearing glasses, and he looked humped and serious over his books, not at all seductive. Nevertheless, when I came in, he kissed me and ruffled my hair. I liked the easy way he did this; it was affectionate as well as sexual. He had a warm body.

I opened the cheese I had brought with me as a present. (It was the same type of cream cheese, covered with raisins, that the Gerbil had had at her birthday party.) Harry didn't seem as delighted by the cheese as I had expected. I went into the kitchen and brought out a plate. Then I cut two slices.

Harry was dominating in his flat. He kept telling me not to leave dead matches all over the place – I had to use them to light the gas – but his own domestic habits left something to be desired. For instance, he peed in the sink, which was our only place for doing dishes, and he farted regularly, seeming rather proud of it. (I was already familiar with crude habits. Throughout my childhood my father, as he left the dining-room at breakfast, more often than not with his pyjama trousers open, would announce to us all that he was off to sit on the lavatory. At intervals during the day, like Harry, my father had emitted terrible foghorn yawns.)

I was also accustomed, because of my father, to being shouted at. But, unlike my father, Harry was always busy. Before he went to work at the agency, he often sat for several hours at his desk writing freelance articles on political events in the various African countries. He had piles of newspaper cuttings, neatly filed, on things that interested him, and whole boxes of letters from his friends. And, most importantly, unlike my father, he never seemed unhappy.

After I had been living in the flat a few days, Harry's shouting got worse. First it was the washing-up – apparently I never cleaned the knives properly. Then he discovered I'd lost a bit of a newspaper with an article of his in it. (I had dropped it in the street.) The third time I was typing in the kitchen and he bellowed as hard as he could because I had left my shoes in his way. I thought perhaps he was agitated because he was in love with me, but this didn't make it any better.

I yelled back, 'I can't stand this shouting any more!'

He said that I had to 'wake up' and not be so messy.

'I don't want to wake up. If I wake up, I can't do my fucking writing, can I?'

'One day when I come back from work, I'm going to find this flat burned down and you just sitting there laughing.'

He filled the dishes with washing-up liquid and left them in the sink.

I decided I hated him, though a quarter of an hour before I had decided I was in love with him. I told him, 'Whatever I've done, you should never shout at people like that. Your other friends may take it because they're all so cringing, but I won't.'

I felt very tired. I lay in my sleeping-bag and put a blanket over my face, while he sat typing at his desk. I thought of other things, putting up a wall in my mind against him. I thought of the garden at my grandmother's, and of her tall pine tree, by which you could always find your way home when lost in the woods. I remembered lying one night in bed at her house, hearing the wind, and imagining I was that tall tree. This image made me immune from Harry's cruelty.

An hour later I got up and started typing a short story.

When Harry went out to work, at about 2 a.m., he said, a bit nervously, 'I shall probably come back immediately after work tomorrow morning.'

I said, 'Well, I won't be here.'

He said, 'Going to find somewhere on your own, are you?'

But the next morning I didn't wake up till he came back. He sat on the bed and read me a letter from his mother, imitating her voice. She wrote that she was sorry for the English miners because their wage wasn't enough to keep a family on. She wrote about her four-year-old grandson, and how he was difficult with his food. I told Harry that he shouldn't mock the letter, and that some of the best writing was about apparently banal things.

I said, 'Look at *Cranford*, though, with your despising literature, you probably haven't heard of it.'

He said, 'Who wrote *Cranford*?'

I said, 'Mrs Gaiskell.'

He said, 'Well, you're wrong, it was Mrs Gaskell.'

Then he went to sleep. I still felt furious, partly because he said he had told the Yellow Hippo, the American journalist, about our quarrels, to prove to her he wasn't in love with me. (He kept being mysterious about the Yellow Hippo, saying she was upset because she had discovered I was living with him, and people didn't do that in her generation. She was ten years older than him.)

I said, 'Well, I don't care if you've balled the Yellow Hippo.'

When he'd gone, I thought about moving to a hotel, but I went and called on Patrick instead, in his tiny room in Montparnasse. He was still lying in his sleeping-bag. The room was filthy and smelled of cigarette smoke. He wouldn't let me open the window. Patrick said, 'I dreamed there was a flood, and you didn't come.'

I thought, it's awful if he minds my coming or not. I said, deliberately quoting from one of his stories, '"I'm tired of fuck." People are always trying to trap me and chase me to fuck me or live with them.'

He said, 'Let me see your cunt.'

I said, 'Of course not.'

I left him later, in a café with an English girl who was wearing Dr Scholl sandals. Some Basque musicians were shouting a brawling song and a weeping Hell's Angel in a silver jacket had draped himself across the bar. I said, 'I'm going home.'

I realized I wanted to get back before Harry left for to work. Patrick took me by the arm and asked when I was coming again. 'Tomorrow?'

I said, 'No, I can't. Maybe Tuesday.'

I felt guilty, because Harry had told me off about being cruel to Patrick, saying that his being lame made it worse. I ran out of the café and up the street, knowing Patrick was probably watching me, and that he would never be able to run.

When I got back to Harry's flat, Harry was still at his desk.

I said, 'Before I came to live here, Anthony asked me, "Are you going out with Patrick?" I didn't know what to say.'

Harry replied, 'You aren't going out with anybody, mate.'

I said, 'I liked Patrick very much again today.'

'You only think that because he's kind and intelligent and will do anything you want.'

I said, 'That's probably true.'

He said, 'I know everything.'

'Your friend Chugga said that. That you thought you knew everything. Can I have some chocolate?'

After eating the chocolate, I added, 'Patrick thinks I look like a chipmunk. He laughed at my cheeks in the Polly Magoo. Chipmunks and hamsters have puffed-out cheeks.'

Harry said, 'Well, I don't think you look like a chipmunk.'

I woke up frightened because I was dreaming about my grandmother's house. I thought, I love this place better than any other place in the world, and I ran down the grass, towards the pond. I looked for a moment with horror at the green water. Then I turned round. A little boy – my dead brother, Jonathan, but he looked like Rose's boyfriend Jake – ran up the bank and across the lawn, taunting me. He glanced back, as if daring me to follow him. I tried to make myself stretch out my arms to him in love, but he eluded me; like Peter Pan, he ran away over the lawn, free, never to grow older, and I was left with my guilt, which was absurd, as I had never done anything to make him drown. I was only seven.

I woke in Harry's room, in my sleeping-bag. It was dark. I was afraid. I wanted to be comforted, but Harry was still on his night shift and might not have been sympathetic anyway.

Later I went back to sleep and dreamed of Peter, my old boyfriend who had accused me of not doing anything positive. In the dream he believed there might be some point in my writing. I asked him if he was still a member of the Communist Party.

Then I dreamed about Patrick, and of him standing naked, with a very white body. His penis had an awful scar on it.

Harry returned from work saying that he had had another quarrel with the Yellow Hippo, in the café where all the journalists drank between shifts.

'The Yellow Hippo walked out on me,' he said.

He stood at the door, while I sat at the kitchen table, without my shirt on, typing.

'She's annoyed because I told her I'd been keeping *two* secrets from her,' Harry went on. 'One is that you're living here, two is that I'm taking the Neanderthal Woman to Africa with me in three weeks' time.'

I did not reply, as I knew this was another of Harry's games to try to make as many women as possible jealous.

He asked if I wanted to fuck.

I usually started by not wanting to make love with Harry as he seemed so aggressive. He would rub my thighs and leap at my back making panting noises, partly as a joke, but partly in seriousness. This put me off. It was as if he weren't waiting for *me* to have any reaction. He wanted me selfishly.

He was good, though. This morning he almost made me unconscious. I thought, there must be some word which would send me over, into peace, but I don't know what it is.

In the dark bed I said, 'Stroke my shoulders.' But it wasn't enough. I thought, probably I don't have that much in common with him. I said to him, 'Whenever I have good sex, I automatically think of my grandmother's.'

I remembered making love with Philippe on the mountain in Crete, and how suddenly the image of a ploughed field, and a train passing through green country, had come into my mind, and I had thought of walking in the fields with my grandmother.

Now, in the dark bed, Harry asked, 'Why?'

'Because it makes me happy, and I'm happy at my grandmother's. It's my home.'

Finale

I went back to England for Christmas. My father had been taken ill. I visited him in hospital. He looked weak and was complaining about the light bulb. He kept saying, 'I tell them the hospital will burn down, but they don't care.'

When the nurse came in, with my red carnations in a vase, he said to her, 'This light must have a weaker bulb.' She took no notice, probably thinking that he was an eccentric or too old to be taken notice of. He was reading the collected letters of Evelyn Waugh. There was a bad smell in the room.

Another nurse came in with the menus. My father said, 'All the food's horrible here. It's coagulated by the time it gets to me. Do you know this hospital costs as much as the Ritz?'

Later my mother told me that my father was very ill and was coming home.

My father was dying, of cirrhosis of the liver. I bought him a red cyclamen in a basket, which then stood beside his bed. My mother had hired a nurse to look after my father. I thought the nurse was like a ghoul, watching over my father till he died. My mother seemed to have given up, leaving everything to the nurse. Was the gap between her and my father too wide for her to be of any practical help or was it that she was so dependent on him that without him she collapsed completely?

My brother was in Nepal with Sheila and there was no way of getting in touch with him.

My grandmother came to stay. She told my mother not to make any decisions for at least a year.

I took my mother's dog, a collie, for a walk in the rain. Raven, my father's dog, had been killed by a car a few weeks earlier, on the road outside my parents' house.

My mother had not put the crib up that year and there was

no Christmas tree either. The nurse presided over tea on Christmas Eve. She cut me two slices of cake.

My father died at lunchtime on Christmas Day. My mother came in, looking white and quiet. She stood by my chair. I did not touch her. I did not want to go upstairs and see my father dead.

Two days later my brother Luke returned. We went to my father's funeral in a big black car. Luke said it was a Rolls, but it looked to me like a hearse. My mother sat in the car between us. She was in black except for a brown fur hat. She looked pale. My brother was in a rented pin-striped suit from Burton. His hair was still very long.

We were the last to arrive at the Catholic church where Luke and I used to go with our father. My mother's cousin Michael was waiting for us on the steps. He took my mother's arm and, forgetting us, led her up to the front of the church. I followed, beckoning to my brother. I felt self-conscious in front of all those people. As I entered the pew, I knocked over a hymn book and a card my mother had had printed, saying my father's name and 'Rest in Peace'.

We were terribly close to the coffin. The flowers looked beautiful. They were mainly yellow flowers. I couldn't remember if my father liked yellow. I had asked for dark-red roses, but there was only one red rose in this bright-yellow sea.

Father O'Hara had retired and now there was a young priest with a chubby face and glasses. Like my mother, he was obsessed with Russia. He was steeped in information about the Russian imperial family; he even knew the names of their dogs. He had once been to a fancy-dress ball dressed as the tsar, in a costume he had made himself. When he came to arrange the funeral, he told my mother that he identified with the tsar – they had had the same sort of upbringing, he explained. Neither had been allowed any responsibilities until the age of twenty-five.

The Mass started. There were two young altar boys. I felt sorry for them, probably seeing a coffin for the first time. I realized then that I should be feeling sorry for myself. It was *my* father who had died.

Intermingled with the Mass were a few Protestant hymns chosen by my mother. 'Lead, kindly Light' was her favourite. There was a great deal of getting up and down.

Soon it was time for Communion. My brother nudged me and said we should go, but I hadn't been for years. Mrs Gaites, the woman who had taught my brother maths at the local primary school, went, and so did Evie the Bespectacled Cod, though she had always been terrified of my father. My mother, a Protestant who only ever received the Communion host in cupped hands, whispered that the communicants reminded her of goldfish, with their eager gaping mouths.

The pall-bearers took up their positions and, with a great deal of pushing and grunting, heaved my father's coffin on to their shoulders. They all had white hair, like my father.

The priest read out a naval prayer, for ships at sea, because my father had been a sailor.

I put a fixed aloof expression on my face and walked out of the church followed by my brother. I saw Ginny, one of the women my father had liked, in a pew, looking very pale. At that moment I hated her.

My brother and I lingered near the church door, not knowing what to do. My mother did not get into the funeral car. People kept coming up and kissing her, then two nuns ran up and, grasping our arms, led all three of us into the priest's quarters, shouting, 'You must see Father O'Hara!'

Father O'Hara, who used to bawl Mass with a hoarse voice, was now over eighty. He was watching coloured television in his sitting-room. He looked bewildered to see us, but shook our hands politely.

My father was being buried in my grandmother's village church, half an hour away, next to my brother Jonathan. At least, this had been my mother's intention, but there was no room for him next to my brother, so he was buried next to my mother's aunt, whom he had found infuriating.

We solemnly followed the coffin over the long grass of the graveyard. There was a view of blue hills. When I saw the open grave, I felt sorry for my father being put in there.

The priest asked me and my mother and brother to sprinkle holy water over the grave, making the sign of the cross. When my brother did it, he looked so absurd with his long hair and rented clothes too big for him that I started to laugh.

At my grandmother's, lunch had been prepared. They had ordered wine and cold meat from the pub. A crowd of people were there, some of whom I did not know. They said they were my father's relations.

My father's first cousin Hester was there. She, like me, had been a pupil at the Sacred Heart, and had then married and divorced, and now lived 'in sin' with a man in a caravan. When I was eleven, Hester had visited us with her terrier bitch, Primrose. I asked how Primrose was now, but she was dead, like my father.

I talked to my grandmother's old chauffeur, Frank, who suffered from a bad heart. When I was five, he had teased me and Jonathan by pretending he didn't know the two times table. He had kept a chart of it in the garage and got it wrong, to make us laugh and to teach us the correct version. Now Frank said to me in his wheezing voice, 'Your father was a brave man. I couldn't have gone in those Arctic convoys.'

I took this as a tribute from one man to another. I offered Frank a whisky, though I guessed his wife would disapprove.

Mrs Gaites, the maths teacher, confided to my grandmother that she had taught my brother in school for three years.

'Well, you didn't make a very good job of it, did you?' said my grandmother sarcastically and unfairly. She knew that my brother was on probation for another drugs offence.

At last everyone left. I stayed with my grandmother on the sofa while my mother, her cousin Michael and Luke drove back to the graveyard. My mother wanted to take photographs of my father's grave.

My mother said to me, 'We're going back up to the grave. Are you coming?'

I said no. I decided never to visit my father's grave again.

I sat with my grandmother on the sofa. Here I felt at peace. There was a beautiful red sky.

My grandmother said, 'When it's spring, we'll all feel much better.'

In January I had lunch with my old friend Andrew, near the office of the oil magazine where he now worked. (He had had to take a regular job again, to help his parents pay their mortgage. He had left the former Lord Radley's commune and was renting a flat with his new boyfriend, an American student.)

I told Andrew, 'I want to be married.'

'You don't, do you?' For some reason, his eyes filled with tears. 'You're bound to feel like that, with your relations dropping dead around you.'

I started dreaming of Paris and longing to go back there. I thought of the bars and cafés I used to go to with Patrick and Anthony. I dreamed about Harry, and of going to sleep in a strawberry bed. I dreamed that Harry and my father met. My father smiled, and encouraged me to see Harry again.

I went back to Paris two months later. (First my mother fell and broke her hip; she, and my brother, were drinking heavily. I couldn't abandon them, though I yearned to return to France.)

Harry was about to leave his room in the Latin Quarter and move to a flat in Montparnasse. He asked if I wanted to live in half of it and share the rent. Afraid that I would lose my independence, I said no. Instead, I took over his old room, paying a monthly rent to his old landlady, whom he called Mrs Pear Tree.

In the Marais too things had changed. A black trumpeter had moved in with Simone, and Anthony was in a cheap hotel in Montmartre. His protected life had ended.

Now he didn't have a home in Paris, his frailty was even more pronounced. One evening we walked up a street near his hotel, a street of transvestite prostitutes. As we passed one of them, he seemed about to weep. I realized he couldn't bear the sordidness, or the tragedy, of much of human existence. I was fascinated by his hyper-sensitivity. This, and his intelligence, gave him an edge, a kind of masculinity which in other aspects he lacked. As I did my brother's, I thought Anthony's intelligence far superior to mine. I felt he was too pure – and perhaps too fragile – for me, yet I was drawn to him.

My grandmother had said, 'When it's spring, we'll all feel much better.'

It's early May and I am sitting by the Seine with Anthony. He gets up to stand by the river. I think, he's perfect. To me, his body's perfect.

He is wearing a black sweater and jeans. He's very lean. I think of what Patrick once said, about Anthony being like Beckett. Although one half of me thinks that Patrick is roman- · ticizing both himself and Anthony, making out that they're artists and poets, it also makes me see Anthony in a special light.

A black dog with long hair shits in front of Anthony. The dog's mistress, wearing high heels and a short coat made with fur from the dog, says, 'That's a compliment, my dog shitting in front of you.'

Anthony murmurs, 'That's the rich for you.'

Then Patrick arrives, wearing a bright-green shirt, carrying a letter and money from his mother in America. When he reads his mother's letter, he becomes childlike. This irritates me and I remember what Harry said, about Los Negativos. It's absurd for someone of thirty to get those letters and cheques from his mother. (Harry's in Africa again for several weeks.)

Later, in a café called Le Petit Bar, a man called Solomon stands very quietly in a corner, not at all like the night before when we'd all been in there, when he had talked loudly about 'a man and a woman'. I think maybe he fancies Patrick.

Then an Arab comes in, an Arab with a black scar over his eye. He says, 'I was leaning out of a window and I was watching a girl's shirt. I leaned over more and more, then I fell out.'

I am amused, but really he got the scar in a fight. I start playing on the pinball machine with a middle-aged Turk.

'OK, Miss!' the Turk shouts.

Anthony is upset because I'm playing with the Turk, not him. He hates to lose. A pessimist. He points out the beautiful tiger lilies on the café window sill.

Later, as we stand against the bar, he says, 'You're not of a melancholic disposition.'

I say, 'No, I'm not.'

He says, pointing to all the tables, at the people looking bored sitting over their drinks, 'They're all dead, like so much dogshit. The trees are alive, like the Seine's alive; the trees and the river, they're the only pure things.'

Out of the window I see that the trees, with their young leaves, that pale-green colour, are moving.

I say, 'I remember my dream now. You and I were in Venice. The end of the dream was that I wrote this good sentence. It was perfect and yet, the odd thing was, the sentence was sad. I had to accept it.'

Anthony says, 'Yes, I see what you mean, just like you said it.'

The Arab with the black scar approaches us and forces our heads together, as if telling us to be lovers.